LANGUAGE ARTS

THE CENTER FOR GIFTED EDUCATION

COLLEGE OF WILLIAM & MARY

Second Edition

Journeys and Destinations

Student GRADES 2-3 Guide

Kendall Hunt
publishing company

Kendall Hunt
publishing company

www.kendallhunt.com
Send all inquiries to:
4050 Westmark Drive
Dubuque, IA 52004-1840
1-800-542-6657

Center for Gifted Education
College of William & Mary
PO Box 8795
Williamsburg, VA 23187-8795
757-221-2362
www.cfge.wm.edu

Funded by the Jacob K. Javits Program, United States Department of Education, under a subcontract from the Washington-Saratoga-Warren-Hamilton-Essex BOCES, Saratoga Springs, New York.

Printed in the United States of America

2 3 4 5 6 7 8 9 10   15 14 13 12 11

Production Date: 6/23/2011
Printed by: Hess Printing Solutions
Woodstock, IL
United States of America
Batch number: 426599-02

Contents

Letter to Student

Dear Student:

You are taking part in a special language arts unit called *Journeys and Destinations*. It includes many activities to help you understand the concept of change.

You will explore the concept of change in many different readings. Discussions, writing, listening, vocabulary study, and research will be based on the readings. In class, we will read and discuss short pieces of literature: poems, short stories, speeches, and essays. You will also read a novel. To clarify your thinking and to help you prepare for written and oral assignments, you will keep a journal. As you read the literature, you will think about its ideas, vocabulary, and structure.

This book includes materials that you will need for this unit. Short stories and poems are in this book, as well as Activity Pages related to all literature selections.

During the unit, you will be using several teaching models. They include:

1. The Literature Web Model

2. The Vocabulary Web Model

3. The Hamburger Model for Persuasive Writing

4. The Writing Process Model

5. The Reasoning Model (including the Reasoning About a Situation or Event Model)

6. The Research Model

Your teacher will explain how these models work and how you can use them as you read the unit literature and complete the required activities.

Sincerely,

Curriculum Development Team

Center for Gifted Education at The College of William and Mary

Glossary of Literary Terms

The following terms may be useful in discussing the unit readings.

Alliteration: a pattern of sound made by repeating consonant at the beginning of words or stressed syllables; for example, *softly slipping on slimy stones.*

Character: a person portrayed in a play or novel; characters can be unique or stereotypical.

Climax: the most exciting part of a story or play, usually happening near the end.

Denouement: the final outcome of a story; the events following the climax.

Dialogue: the conversation between characters in a play or story.

Dynamic character: a character who grows or matures throughout the course of a story.

Figurative language: the use of analogies, metaphors, or similes that describe something by comparing it with something else.

Free verse: verse in which the meter and line length vary and with no rhyme pattern.

Imagery: words or phrases that give sensory images that help a reader to see characters, scenes, or events in a poem or story in his or her imagination.

Metaphor: a type of figurative language in which two things are compared. One thing is said to be the other; for example, *The girl is a ray of sunshine.*

Motivation: the reasons or desires that cause a character in a story to act.

Narrator: the speaker or voice that tells a story.

Plot: the series of events in a story.

Point of view: the position from which a narrator tells a story, either within the story (first person) or as an outside observer (third person).

Protagonist: the main character.

Repetition: the repeating of a word or a pattern for effect.

Setting: the time and place in which a story takes place.

Simile: a type of figurative language in which two things are compared using the words *like* or *as*; for example, *Her mind was as sharp as a blade.*

Stanza: a group of lines of verse within a song or poem.

Static character: a character who remains unchanged by the events of a story, so that he or she is basically the same at the end as at the beginning.

Symbol: an image, word, or object that stands for something greater than itself; the image is usually visible, but what it represents is often invisible. For example, the flag is a symbol of patriotism.

Theme: the central idea of a poem, short story, or novel.

Voice: the perspective of the narrator of the story.

Models

The Literature Web Model

The Literature Web is a model that can help you understand what you read. It encourages you to connect your personal responses with the text. You may complete the web on your own, with a group, or whole class. Note the following kinds of ideas in each of the four parts of the web:

Key Words: interesting, unfamiliar, or important words and phrases in the text

Feelings: the reader's feelings, including parts of the text that inspired them; the characters' feelings; and the feelings the author may have hoped to inspire

Ideas: major themes and main ideas of the text; key concepts

Images and Symbols: important images in the text; "pictures" in the reader's mind and the text that inspired them; symbols for bigger ideas

A fifth part may be added to the web for an extra challenge.

Structure: the form, shape, or organization of the writing and how these add to the meaning; features such as use of unusual time sequence (flashbacks), use of voice, use of figurative language, etc.; style of writing

Literature Web Model

Key Words

_____

_____

_____

_____

Feelings

_____

_____

_____

_____

Title

_____

_____

_____

Ideas

_____

_____

_____

_____

Images or Symbols

_____

_____

_____

_____

The Vocabulary Web Model

The Vocabulary Web is a tool for exploring a word in depth. Find the definition of the word and its part of speech, synonyms, and antonyms word stems, and origin. Then try to find at least three other members of the same word family, words that use one or more of the same stems. Then create a sentence, analogy, picture, or diagram that illustrates your word. Use the Vocabulary Web to organize your responses.

Vocabulary Web Model

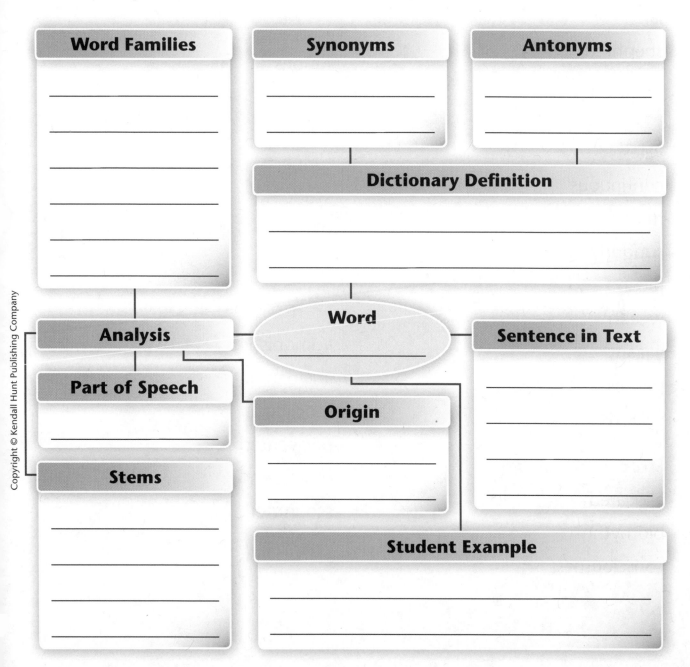

Unit vocabulary words you may want to explore include:

From "The Wolf and the Lion":

evil

excuse

inconvenience

injure

lair

shepherd

From "I Wandered Lonely as a Cloud":

vales

continuous

margin

sprightly

jocund

wealth

vacant

pensive

solitude

From *The Green Book:*

allocated

biorhythms

consciousness

flagons

fodder

hexagon

hostile

malfunction

perishable

rapt

rations

relevant

rivulet

runnel

scudding

treacle

wistfully

From "The Ugly Duckling":

admonished

aristocratic

mocked

persecuted

probation

scoundrel

From *Bringing the Rain to Kapiti Plain:*

migrated

pasture

stork

From "Ozymandias":

antique

visage

sculptor

passion

pedestal

despair

colossal

boundless

From *Sachiko Means Happiness:*

crossly

impatiently

reassure

reflected

timidly

From "The Green Man":

arrogant

defiant

glean

tether

From "Nurse's Song":

besides

echo

dale

pale

disguise

The Hamburger Model for Persuasive Writing

The Hamburger Model compares writing a paragraph or essay with making a sandwich. You begin by stating your point of view (the top bun). You then provide at least three reasons for your point of view (the "patties"). Then you provide elaboration, or additional details, for each of your reasons (the "fixings"). A concluding sentence or paragraph closes the piece of writing (the bottom bun).

Hamburger Model for Persuasive Writing

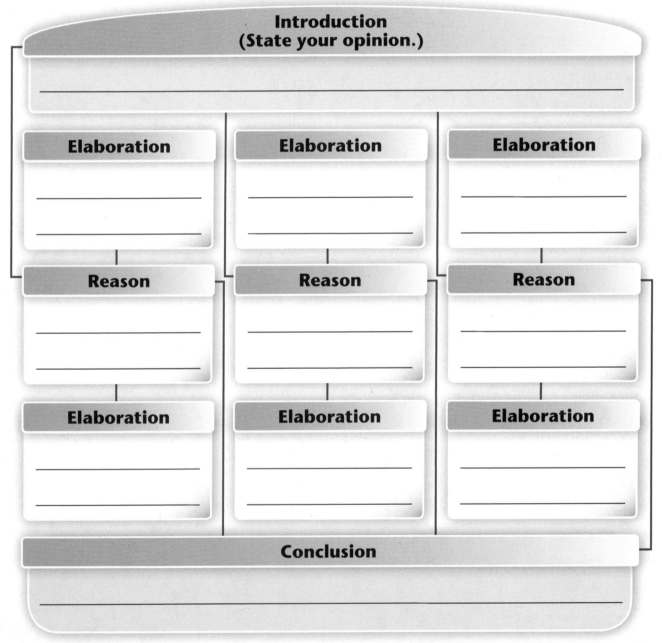

The Reasoning Model

Paul's Elements of Reasoning (1992) can help you think and argue better. It has eight parts, or elements: *issue, purpose, point of view, assumptions, concepts, evidence, inferences,* and *implications or consequences.* Use these elements whenever you need to write about or think through issues and problems.

Here is a description of each element:

1. **Purpose, Goal, or End View**

   We reason for a purpose—to achieve a goal, satisfy a desire, or meet a need. For example, if there are no eggs or milk in your refrigerator one morning, the purpose of your reasoning would be to figure out what else to make for breakfast. If there is a problem with your purpose, then there will be problems with your reasoning. For example, if your goal is unrealistic, in conflict with your other goals, or confused in some way, then the reasoning you use to meet that goal will have problems. On the other hand, if you are clear about the purpose for your reasoning, it will help you focus your thoughts. For example, the purpose of your reasoning might be to persuade others to do something. If you are clear about this purpose, then your persuasive writing and speaking on this topic will be focused and therefore more effective. Similarly, when you read and listen to what others say or write, you should be able to determine their purpose.

2. **Question at Issue (or Problem to Be Solved)**

   When we attempt to reason about something, there is at least one question at issue or problem to be solved. In fact, without a question or problem, no reasoning is needed! If you are not clear about what the question or problem is, it is unlikely that you will find an answer that serves your purpose. As part of the reasoning process, you should be able to state the question to be answered or the problem to be solved, such as, "What else can I use to make breakfast?" or, "Should teachers assign homework on weekends?"

Adapted from Paul, R. (1992). Critical thinking: What every person needs to survive in a rapidly changing world. *CA: Foundation for Critical Thinking.*

3. Points of View or Frame of Reference

As we reason about an issue, we are influenced by our own point of view. For example, teachers and students may have different points of view about homework. Another example is that the price of a shirt may seem low to one person and high to another. Any problem in your point of view is a possible source of problems in your reasoning. Your point of view may be too narrow, not specific enough, or unfair. By keeping in mind the points of view of others, you can sharpen or broaden your thinking. Similarly, in writing and speaking, you can strengthen your argument by addressing other points of view. In listening and reading, you need to identify the point of view of the speaker or author and understand how it affects the message.

4. Experiences, Data, Evidence

When we reason, we must be able to support our point of view with evidence, or supporting facts. Evidence can come from surveys, published studies, nonfiction books, or even from your own experiences. The use of evidence helps you to see the difference between reasons and opinions, make good judgments, and strengthen your arguments. In reading and listening, you can judge whether or not an argument is strong by looking carefully at the supporting data or evidence. Experience can also provide evidence or data. For example, your experience making breakfast yesterday might help you in the process of figuring out what to make for breakfast today.

5. Concepts and Ideas

When you reason, you must understand the concepts and big ideas that have to do with the problem. These concepts can include definitional terms, principles, rules, or theories. When you read or listen, you can ask yourself, "What key ideas are being presented?" When you write or speak, you can organize your thoughts around certain concepts and ideas. Some examples of concepts are freedom, friendship, and responsibility.

6. Assumptions

An assumption is a belief that may not have any proof. When we reason, we need to be aware of the assumptions we have made and the assumptions of others. If we make bad assumptions, this can lead to problems in our reasoning. As a writer or speaker we make assumptions about our audience and our message. For example, we might assume that others will share our point of view; or we might assume that the audience already knows all the details about our topic. As a reader or listener we should be able to identify the assumptions of the writer or speaker.

7. Inferences

Reasoning happens through small steps of the mind called inferences. An inference is a conclusion that something is true because something else is true. The inferences you make depend on the data you have and your assumptions. For example, if you see dark clouds, you might infer that it is going to rain. Or if it is now 6:45 and it takes 30 minutes to get to the movie theater, you will probably conclude that you cannot get to the theater in time for a 7:00 movie. Many inferences are reasonable, but many are not. You need to be able to tell the difference between the data you observe and the inferences you make about it. Also, be aware that the inferences you make can be influenced by your point of view and assumptions.

8. Implications and Consequences

Good reasoning means thinking about the implications and consequences of your point of view and actions. Similarly, when you read or listen to an argument, you need to ask yourself what follows from that way of thinking. You can also consider consequences of actions that characters in stories take, just as you can consider consequences of your own actions. For example, if you don't do your homework, then you might have to stay after school to complete it; or, if your water you lawn, it may not wither in the summer heat.

Reasoning Model

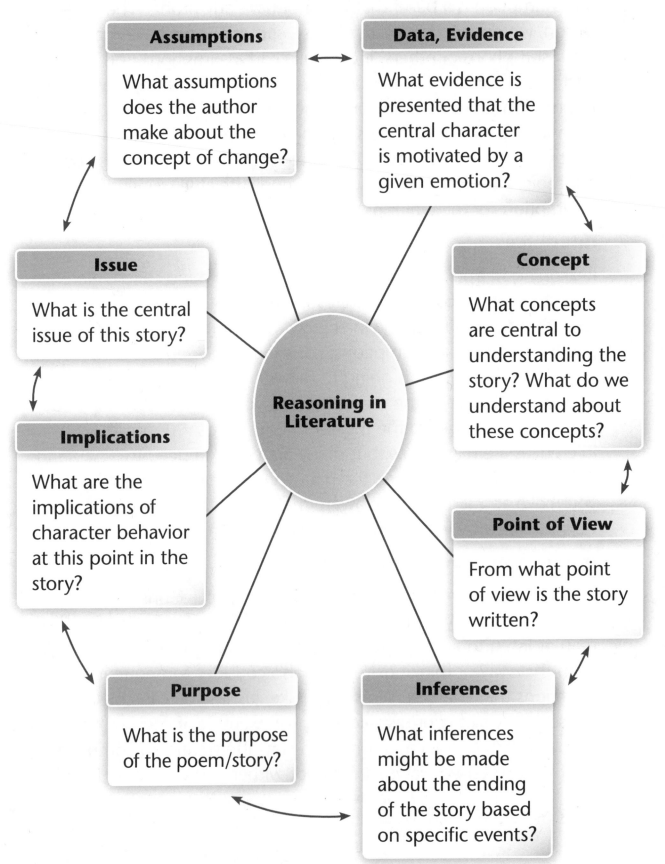

The Writing Process Model

The Writing Process describes the stages that writers go through to develop a piece of writing. The stages are not separate steps you have to go through from one to five; you can move back and forth among the stages to help you construct, clarify, and polish their writing. The Writing Process Model is used throughout the unit to help you to improve your writing.

The following are the stages of the Writing Process:

1. *Prewriting:* List your ideas and begin to organize them. You may want to use a graphic organizer such as a web or Venn diagram. Graphic organizers help you to see what you will write about. As you write, you can add to your graphic organizer or change it.

2. *Drafting:* Write a rough draft, getting your ideas onto paper and not worrying about mechanics such as spelling, grammar, or punctuation. Some writers call this stage "composing." Sometimes this stage is a "messing around" stage in which your drafting or composing helps you to "hear" what you want to say.

3. *Revising:* Ask people (friends, family, teachers) to read and listen to your work and to tell you what they like, what they'd like to know more about, and what they don't understand. This is the place to make major changes in your draft. Sometimes you may want to go back to the prewriting stage and redo your graphic organizer to give your paper a new structure.

4. *Editing:* After you have revised your paper, look for the small changes that will make a big difference. Check your choice of words and identify mechanical errors. After you make the changes and corrections, proofread your work one final time. You may want to ask a friend or an adult for help.

5. *Sharing or publishing:* There are many ways to share and to publish your work. You can bind it into a book, copy it in your best handwriting and post it on a bulletin board, read it aloud to your class or family, or make it into a gift for someone special.

The Research Model

The Research Model gives you a way to approach an issue and explore it. It's based on the Elements of Reasoning.

1. **Identify your issue or problem.**
   - What is the issue or problem?
   - Who are the stakeholders and what are their positions?
   - What is my position on this issue?

2. **Read about your issue and identify points of view or arguments through information sources.**
   - What are my print sources?
   - What are my media sources?
   - What are my people sources?
   - What primary and secondary source documents might I use?
   - What are my preliminary findings based on a review of existing sources?

3. **Form a set of questions that can be answered by a specific set of data.**
   - What would be the results of _____?
   - Who would benefit and by how much?
   - Who would be harmed and by how much?
   - My research questions:

4. **Gather evidence through research methods such as surveys, interviews, or information of primary and secondary source documents.**
   - What survey questions should I ask?
   - What interview questions should I ask?

Journeys and Destinations · Models

- What generalizations do secondary sources give?
- What data and evidence can I find in primary sources to support different sides of the issue?

5. **Manipulate and transform data so that they can be interpreted.**

- How can I summarize what I learned?
- Should I develop charts, diagrams, or graphs to represent my data?

6. **Draw conclusions and make inferences.**

- What do the data mean? How can I interpret what I found out?
- How do the data support my original point of view?
- How do they support other points of view?
- What conclusions can I make about the issue?
- What is my point of view now, based on the data?

7. **Determine implications and consequences.**

- What are the consequences of following the point of view that I support?
- Do I know enough or are there now new questions to be answered?

8. **Communicate your findings. (Prepare an oral presentation for classmates based on notes and written report.)**

- What are my purpose, issue, and point of view, and how will I explain them?
- What data will I use to support my point of view?
- How will I conclude my presentation?

The Wolf and the Lion

A fable by Aesop

A Wolf had stolen a Lamb and was carrying it off to his lair to eat it. But his plans were very much changed when he met a Lion, who, without making any excuses, took the Lamb away from him.

The Wolf made off to a safe distance, and then said in a much injured tone:

"You have no right to take my property like that!"

The Lion looked back, but as the Wolf was too far away to be taught a lesson without too much inconvenience, he said:

"Your property? Did you buy it, or did the Shepherd make you a gift of it? Pray tell me, how did you get it?"

What is evil won is evil lost.

Name: _____ Date: _____

 **Activity 1A**

Literature Web

Directions: Complete the Literature Web for "The Wolf and the Lion."

Key Words
_____
_____
_____
_____

Feelings
_____
_____
_____
_____

Title
_____
_____
_____

Ideas
_____
_____
_____
_____

Images or Symbols
_____
_____
_____
_____

Name: _____ Date: _____

Draw a Moral

Directions: Illustrate three events from "The Wolf and the Lion" that tell the moral of the story without using words.

Name: _____ Date: _____

Change Model

Directions: Write two or more examples for each generalization.

Change

> ### Change is linked to time.
> _____
> _____

> ### Change is everywhere.
> _____
> _____

> ### Change may be positive or negative.
> _____
> _____

> ### Change may be perceived as orderly or random.
> _____
> _____

> ### Change may happen naturally or may be caused by people.
> _____
> _____

Name: _____ Date: _____

 **Activity
2B**

Directions: Measure the temperature outside five days in a row. Measure the temperature at the same time each day. Write the time in the title of the chart. Write each day and temperature on the chart. After five days, make a line graph showing the temperatures. Write the generalization that the changes in temperature show.

| The Temperature at _____. ||
Day	**Temperature**

The Temperature at _____.

Temperature

Day

Generalization About Change:

_____

_____

_____

_____

_____

_____

_____

Activity
3A

Literature Web

Directions: Complete the Literature Web for *The Memory String*.

Key Words
_____
_____
_____
_____

Feelings
_____
_____
_____
_____

Title
_____
_____
_____

Ideas
_____
_____
_____
_____

Images or Symbols
_____
_____
_____
_____

Name: _____ Date: _____

 **Activity**
3B

Change Matrix

Directions: Use this chart to make notes about changes you notice in each story or poem.

Literature	Changes in characters	Changes in setting
The Memory String		
"I Wandered Lonely as a Cloud"		
The Green Book		
"poem for rodney," "Poem," and "Perfection"		
"The Ugly Duckling"		
Bringing the Rain to Kapiti Plain		
"Ozymandias"		
Sachiko Means Happiness		
"The Green Man"		
Two versions of "Nurse's Song"		
Your own story		

Journeys and Destinations · Lesson 3 · Reinforcement of Literature Interpretation Skills

	Changes in relationships	**Changes in you as a result of reading**
The Memory String		
"I Wandered Lonely as a Cloud"		
The Green Book		
""poem for rodney," "Poem," and "Perfection"		
"The Ugly Duckling"		
Bringing the Rain to Kapiti Plain		
"Ozymandias"		
Sachiko Means Happiness		
"The Green Man"		
Two versions of "Nurse's Song"		
Your own story		

Name: _____ Date: _____

 **Activity**
3C

Compare and Contrast Characters

Directions: Use the Venn diagram to compare and contrast a young character in another Eve Bunting book with Laura. Write ways they are alike in the middle part of the diagram and ways they are different in the outer parts.

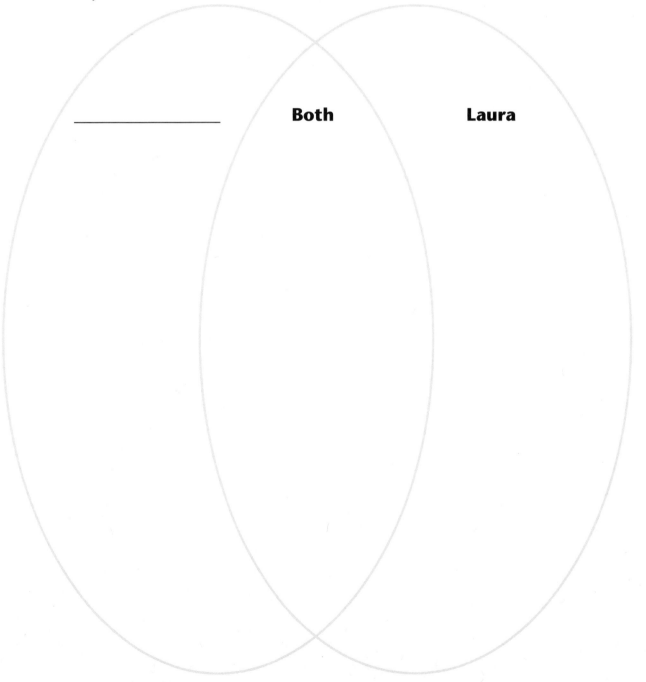

_____   **Both**   **Laura**

Name: _____ Date: _____

Vocabulary Web

Directions: Complete the Vocabulary Web for the word "shepherd."

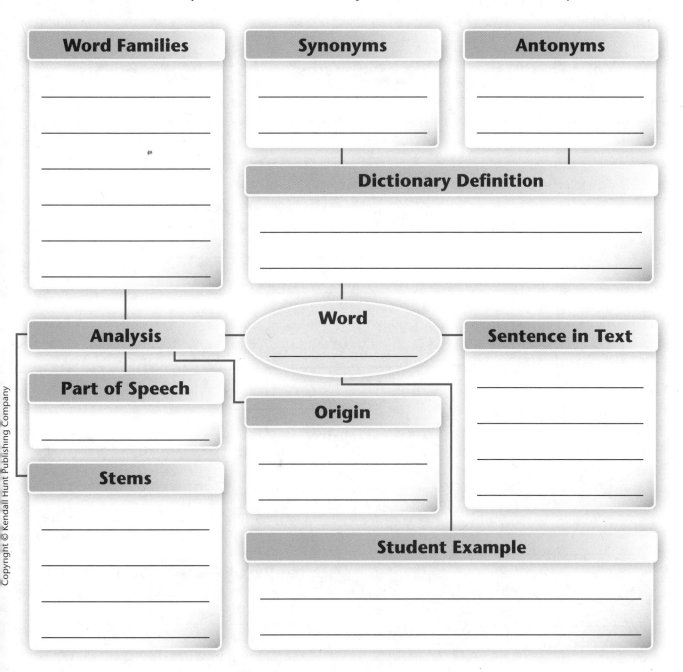

Word Families

_____

_____

_____

_____

_____

Synonyms

_____

_____

Antonyms

_____

_____

Dictionary Definition

_____

_____

Analysis

Word

_____

Sentence in Text

_____

_____

_____

Part of Speech

_____

Origin

_____

Stems

_____

_____

_____

Student Example

_____

_____

Name: _____ Date: _____

Activity
4B

Vocabulary Web

Directions: Complete the Vocabulary Web for the word assigned to you.

Word Families	Synonyms	Antonyms

Dictionary Definition

Word

Analysis

Sentence in Text

Part of Speech

Origin

Stems

Student Example

Name: _____ Date: _____

Write a New Title for
The Memory String

Activity
4C

Directions: Choose a new title for *The Memory String*.
Then complete the sentences.

My new title for *The Memory String* is _____

_____

_____.

I came up with the title by _____

_____

_____.

One reason I chose the title is _____

_____

_____.

Another reason I chose the title is _____

_____

_____.

Activity
4D

Alliteration Poem

Directions: Choose a word up to nine letters long. Write the letters of the word in the boxes. You may not need to use all the boxes. Then write two words that begin with that letter next to the letter in each box. The words in the blanks should describe the word in the boxes.

Name: _____ Date: _____

The Hamburger Model for Persuasive Writing

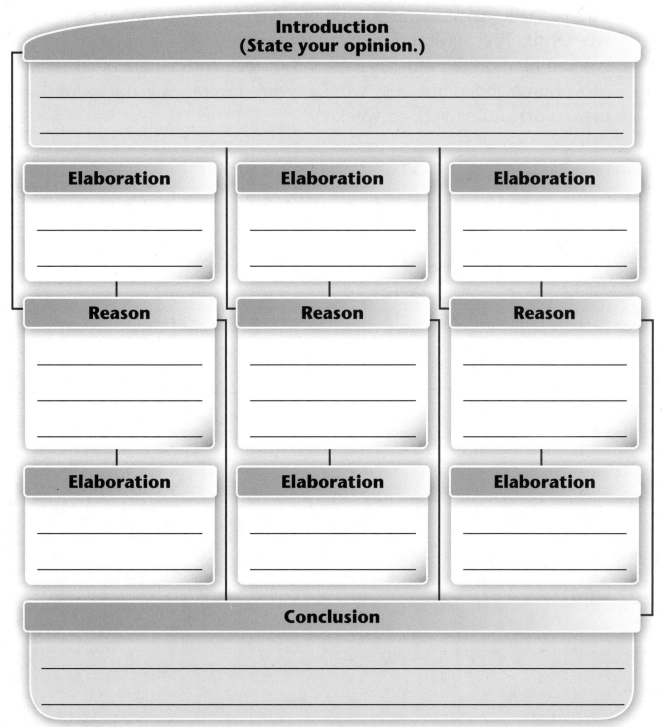

Introduction
(State your opinion.)

_____
_____

Elaboration	**Elaboration**	**Elaboration**
_____	_____	_____
_____	_____	_____

Reason	**Reason**	**Reason**
_____	_____	_____
_____	_____	_____

Elaboration	**Elaboration**	**Elaboration**
_____	_____	_____
_____	_____	_____

Conclusion

_____
_____

Name: _____ Date: _____

I don't think that students should be given homework on the weekends. They have too many other things to do. They have worked hard on the other nights of the week and need a break. Most homework is just busy work anyway. Overall, it is not a good idea to give homework on weekends.

Jumbled Paragraph

Directions: Cut out each sentence. Put the sentences in the best order. Use the Hamburger Model to help you.

I would have to feed it and take it for a walk every day.

It would also scare away strangers who are up to no good.

I think that we should get a dog for a pet.

Second, it would keep me company when there is no one else to play with me.

So you see, having a dog would be a good thing for our family.

First, it would help me learn to be responsible.

Name: _____ Date: _____

No Dog!

Directions: Think of reasons why a parent might not want a dog for a family pet. Use the Hamburger Model to organize the reasons. Then write a paragraph from the point of view of a parent who does not want a dog.

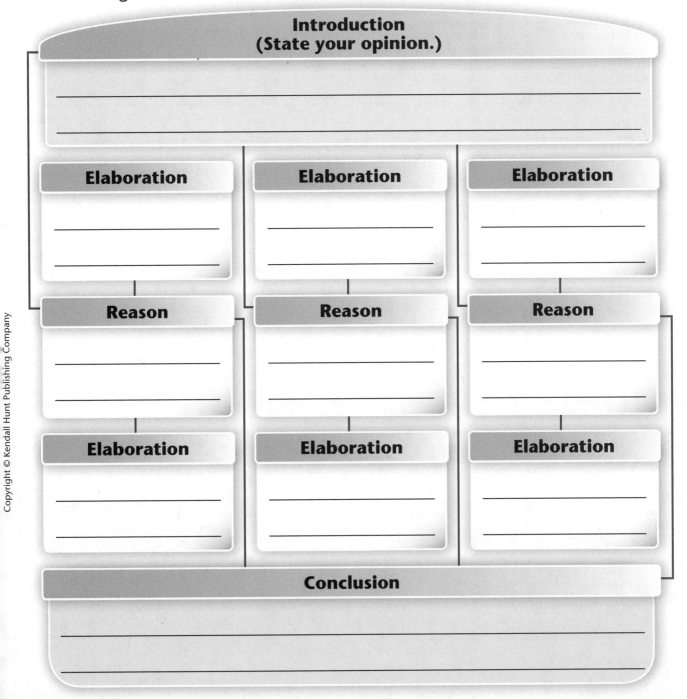

Introduction
(State your opinion.)

Elaboration	**Elaboration**	**Elaboration**

Reason	**Reason**	**Reason**

Elaboration	**Elaboration**	**Elaboration**

Conclusion

Activity
5E

Let's Make a Change

Directions: Think of something about your class that you would like changed. Then think of reasons that might convince your teacher to make the change. Use the Hamburger Model to organize your reasons. Then write a letter to persuade your teacher to make the change.

Introduction
(State your opinion.)

Elaboration	Elaboration	Elaboration

Reason	Reason	Reason

Elaboration	Elaboration	Elaboration

Conclusion

Name: _____ Date: _____
Name: _____ Date: _____

Elements of
Reasoning Practice

Activity
6A
Activity
6A

Directions: Discuss "Teacher Response to Homework on the
Weekend" with your group. Then answer the questions.

Issue or problem: What is the problem?

_____

_____

Purpose or goal: What is the purpose of the teacher's response?

_____

_____

Point of view: What would each of the people involved think about
the problem?

_____

_____

Experiences, data, or evidence: What information will help you to
make your decision?

_____

_____

Copyright © Kendall Hunt Publishing Company
Copyright © Kendall Hunt Publishing Company

Journeys and Destinations · Lesson 6 · Writing and Thinking   41

Assumptions: What assumptions might you make?

_____

_____

Concepts or ideas: What ideas are involved in this problem?

_____

_____

Inferences (or small conclusions): What are the small conclusions you can make based on the facts you have?

_____

_____

Implications and consequences: What are some possible consequences for the teacher and the students, depending on the decision that is made?

_____

_____

Standards of
Reasoning Practice

Activity
6B

Directions: Answer these questions and decide whether or not good reasoning is used in "Teacher Response to Homework on the Weekend."

Are there enough reasons to make a convincing argument? Explain your answer.

_____

_____

Is the evidence correct or right? Give an example that supports your response.

_____

_____

Are the reasons clear or is more information needed? Give an example of a reason that you think is unclear. What information is needed to make it clearer?

_____

_____

Are the reasons or examples specific? Give an example to support your answer.

_____

_____

Are the arguments and reasons strong and important? Or are they weak? Give an example to support your response.

_____

_____

Does the thinking make sense? Do the sentences seem to be in the correct order?

_____

_____

I Wandered Lonely as a Cloud

William Wordsworth

I wandered lonely as a cloud
That floats on high o'er vales and hills,
When all at once I saw a crowd,
A host, of golden daffodils;
Beside the lake, beneath the trees,
Fluttering and dancing in the breeze.

Continuous as the stars that shine
And twinkle on the Milky Way,
They stretched in never-ending line
Along the margin of a bay:
Ten thousand saw I at a glance,
Tossing their heads in sprightly dance.

The waves beside them danced; but they
Outdid the sparkling waves in glee;
A poet could not but be gay
In such a jocund company;
I gazed—and gazed—but little thought
What wealth to me the show had brought.

For oft, when on my couch I lie
In vacant or in pensive mood,
They flash upon that inward eye
Which is the bliss of solitude;
And then my heart with pleasure fills,
And dances with the daffodils.

Name: _____ Date: _____

Vocabulary Web

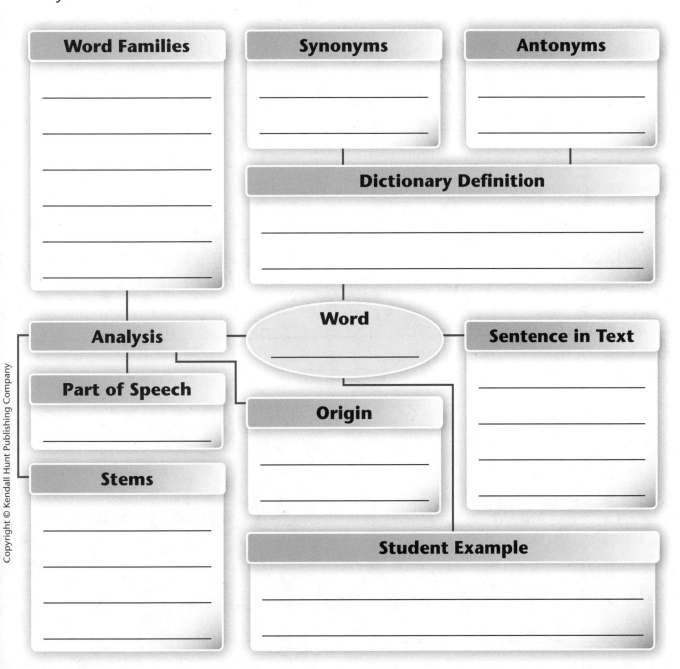

Activity
7A

Directions: Complete the Vocabulary Web for the word assigned to you.

Word Families	**Synonyms**	**Antonyms**

Dictionary Definition

Analysis

Part of Speech

Stems

Word

Origin

Sentence in Text

Student Example

Name: _____ Date: _____

 **Activity**
7B

Literature Web

Directions: Complete the Literature Web for "I Wandered Lonely as a Cloud."

Key Words	Feelings
_____	_____
_____	_____
_____	_____
_____	_____

Title

_____

_____

_____

Ideas	Images or Symbols
_____	_____
_____	_____
_____	_____
_____	_____

A New Title for "I Wandered Lonely as a Cloud"?

Directions: With your class, you will write a paragraph to answer the question, *Should "I Wandered Lonely as a Cloud" be renamed "Change and Memory"?* First, write your own ideas for the paragraph. Complete the sentences to help you develop your ideas.

One of the things that make a title good is _____

_____.

"I Wandered Lonely as a Cloud" is a good title because _____

_____.

"Change and Memory" could be a good title because _____

_____.

The title I like better is _____

because _____

_____ ,

and _____

_____.

Name: _____   Date: _____

Literature Web

Directions: Complete the Literature Web for Chapters 1 and 2 of
The Green Book.

<table>
<tr><td>

Key Words

_____

_____

_____

_____

</td><td>

Feelings

_____

_____

_____

_____

</td></tr>
</table>

Title

_____

_____

_____

<table>
<tr><td>

Ideas

_____

_____

_____

_____

</td><td>

Images or Symbols

_____

_____

_____

_____

</td></tr>
</table>

Name: _____ Date: _____

Activity
8B

Compare and Contrast
Earth and the New Planet

Directions: Use the Venn diagram to compare and contrast Earth and the New Planet. Write ways they are alike in the middle part and ways they are different in the outer parts.

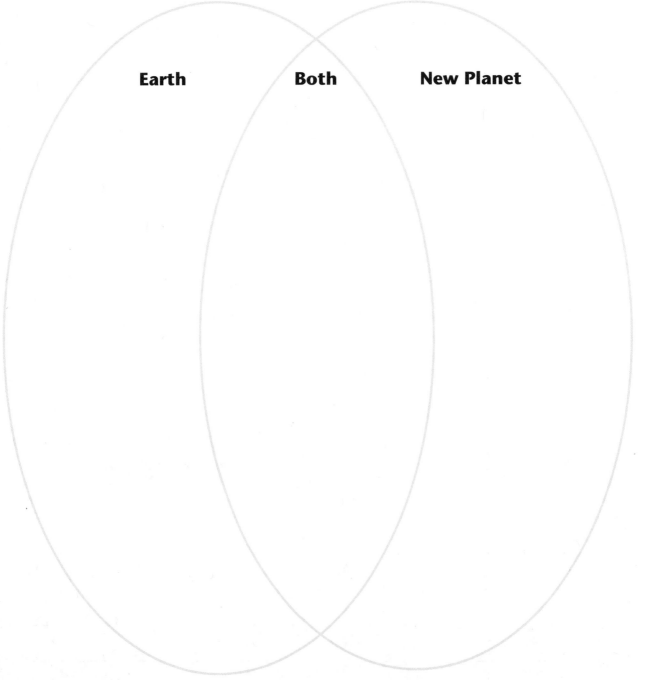

Earth   **Both**   **New Planet**

Name: _____ Date: _____

Time Capsule

Directions: In each box, write two things that you think should go in a time capsule.

Technology	Music and Art
Buildings and Homes	**Family**
Education	**Books, Stories, and Poems**

Name: _____ Date: _____

Activity
8D

Vocabulary Web

Directions: Complete the Vocabulary Web for the word assigned to you.

Word Families
_____
_____
_____
_____

Synonyms
_____
_____

Antonyms
_____
_____

Dictionary Definition
_____

Word
_____

Analysis

Part of Speech
_____

Stems
_____
_____

Origin
_____
_____

Sentence in Text
_____
_____
_____

Student Example
_____
_____

Journeys and Destinations · Lesson 8 · The Green Book

Literature Web

Directions: Complete the Literature Web for Chapters 3 and 4 of *The Green Book*.

Key Words	Feelings
_____	_____
_____	_____
_____	_____
_____	_____

Title

_____
_____
_____

Ideas	Images or Symbols
_____	_____
_____	_____
_____	_____
_____	_____

Name: _____ Date: _____

Activity
9B

Brainstorm

Directions: Imagine that you are moving with your family to a new home in another state. Make a web to help you think of things you would want to take with you to help you remember a special person, place, or time.

Things to take to a new home

Suppose you learn that you cannot take everything with you to the new home. Choose the most important thing to take with you. Circle it.

The Hamburger Model for Persuasive Writing

Activity 9C

Directions: Think about the object you would most want to take with you to a new home in another state. Think of reasons why you would take it. Use the Hamburger Model to organize your reasons. Then write a paragraph on a separate sheet of paper telling what you would take and why.

**Introduction
(State your opinion.)**

_____
_____

Elaboration	**Elaboration**	**Elaboration**
_____	_____	_____
_____	_____	_____

Reason	**Reason**	**Reason**
_____	_____	_____
_____	_____	_____

Elaboration	**Elaboration**	**Elaboration**
_____	_____	_____
_____	_____	_____

Conclusion

_____
_____

Name: _____ Date: _____

 **Activity**
9D

Directions: Below each quotation, write what you think it means.

Neither a borrower nor a lender be,
For loan oft loses both itself and friend …
   —*Hamlet*

_____

_____

_____

All that glisters is not gold …
   —*The Merchant of Venice*

_____

_____

_____

See how she leans her cheek upon her hand!
O that I were a glove upon that hand
That I might touch that cheek.
   —*Romeo and Juliet*

_____

_____

_____

What's in a name? That which we call a rose
By any other name would smell as sweet.
   —*Romeo and Juliet*

_____

_____

_____

All the world's a stage,
And all the men and women merely players:
They have their exits and their entrances;
And one man in his time plays many parts,
His acts being seven ages.
   —*As You Like It*

_____

_____

_____

Name: _____ Date: _____

 **Activity**
9E

Vocabulary Web

Directions: Complete the Vocabulary Web for the word assigned to you.

Word Families
_____
_____
_____
_____
_____

Synonyms
_____
_____

Antonyms
_____
_____

Dictionary Definition
_____
_____

Analysis

Part of Speech
_____

Stems
_____
_____

Word
_____

Origin
_____
_____

Sentence in Text
_____
_____
_____

Student Example
_____
_____

Copyright © Kendall Hunt Publishing Company

Name: _____ Date: _____

Literature Web

Directions: Complete the Literature Web for Chapter 5 of
The Green Book.

Key Words	**Feelings**
_____	_____
_____	_____
_____	_____
_____	_____

Title

_____

_____

_____

Ideas	**Images or Symbols**
_____	_____
_____	_____
_____	_____
_____	_____

Name: _____ Date: _____

 **Activity 10B**

Self-Review of Writing

Assignment: _____

Directions: For each sentence, circle the choice that best describes your writing. Then complete the two sentences.

1. My main idea is clear.

   Needs improvement   Satisfactory   Excellent

2. My details support the main idea.

   Needs improvement   Satisfactory   Excellent

3. My ideas flow smoothly and are in an order that makes sense.

   Needs improvement   Satisfactory   Excellent

4. The structure clearly follows the Hamburger Model (introduction, body, conclusion).

   Needs improvement   Satisfactory   Excellent

5. My vocabulary is rich and varied.

   Needs improvement   Satisfactory   Excellent

   My writing is strong in these ways:

   _____

   _____

   _____

My writing could be improved in these ways:

_____

_____

_____

Name: _____ Date: _____

Activity 10C

Peer Review of Writing

Directions: For each sentence, circle the choice that best describes your partner's writing. Then complete the two sentences.

1. The main idea is clear.

    Needs improvement   Satisfactory   Excellent

2. The details support the main idea.

    Needs improvement   Satisfactory   Excellent

3. The ideas flow smoothly and are in an order that makes sense.

    Needs improvement   Satisfactory   Excellent

4. The structure clearly follows the Hamburger Model (introduction, body, conclusion).

    Needs improvement   Satisfactory   Excellent

5. The vocabulary is rich and varied.

    Needs improvement   Satisfactory   Excellent

The writing is strong in these ways:

_____

_____

_____

The writing could be improved in these ways:

_____

_____

_____

Name: _____ Date: _____

Activity 10D

Vocabulary Web

Directions: Complete the Vocabulary Web for the word assigned to you.

Word Families
_____
_____
_____
_____
_____

Synonyms
_____
_____

Antonyms
_____
_____

Dictionary Definition
_____
_____

Word
_____

Analysis

Part of Speech
_____

Stems
_____
_____

Origin
_____
_____

Sentence in Text
_____
_____
_____

Student Example
_____
_____

Name: _____ Date: _____

Compare and Contrast
Moving Items

Directions: Use the Venn diagram to compare and contrast the items you would take if you were moving to a new state and those you would take if you were moving to a new planet. Write items you would take to both places in the middle part of the diagram. Write items you would take only to one place or the other in the outer parts.

New State　　　　**Both**　　　　**New Planet**

Literature Web

Directions: Complete the Literature Web for Chapters 6 and 7 of *The Green Book*.

Key Words

_____

_____

_____

_____

Feelings

_____

_____

_____

Title

_____

_____

_____

Ideas

_____

_____

_____

_____

Images or Symbols

_____

_____

_____

_____

Name: _____ Date: _____

Activity
11B

Change Model

Directions: Write two examples from *The Green Book* for each generalization. You may draw your examples.

Change is linked to time.

_____

_____

Change is everywhere.

_____

_____

Change may be positive or negative.

_____

_____

Change

Change may be perceived as orderly or random.

_____

_____

Change may happen naturally or may be caused by people.

_____

_____

Name: _____ Date: _____

Concept Web: Remembering

Directions: Create a Concept Web about remembering.

Remembering

Name: _____ Date: _____

Activity 11D

Research Assignment

Directions: For this assignment, you will complete several different tasks.

Part 1

There are many ways to preserve memories or to keep important things from being forgotten. Brainstorm some of the ways people preserve memories. How many can you name? (Examples include diaries, photograph albums, paintings and drawings, stories, video tapes, books, audio tape recordings, religious festivals and rituals, initials carved in trees, museum collections, libraries, copy machines, etc.) Which of these ways require technology such as electricity or computers? Divide your list into two groups: traditional methods that do not depend on technology and modern methods that use technology. What are the advantages and disadvantages of each type?

Part 2

Choose a point of view about the best ways to preserve memories. Do some research to support your point of view. Your research might include library materials, interviews, or a survey.

Part 3

Later in this unit you will write a short paper (one to two pages) and give a two-minute presentation on your point of view, supported by your findings. You will write this paper using the Hamburger Model structure, just as you have practiced writing paragraphs in class.

Name: _____ Date: _____

How to Preserve Memories

Directions: Brainstorm a list of the ways people preserve memories. Then organize your list into two types—methods that require technology and methods that do not require technology. Finally, describe the advantages and disadvantages of each type.

1. Brainstorm a list of ways people preserve memories.

2. Write each of the ways in the correct category.

Technology	No Technology

3. What are the advantages and disadvantages of preserving memories *with* technology? What are the advantages and disadvantages of preserving memories *without* technology?

Preserving Memories *with* Technology	
Advantages	**Disadvantages**

Preserving Memories *without* Technology	
Advantages	**Disadvantages**

Research Model Planner

Directions: Use this planner to help you research your issue. You may write your answers on another sheet of paper so that you have enough space for all of your ideas. Do your best to answer each question now. You may need make changes to your planner later.

1. **Identify the issue or problem.**

   • What is the issue or problem?

   _____

   _____

   • Who are the stakeholders and what are their positions?

   _____

   _____

   • What is my position on this issue?

   _____

   _____

2. Read about your issue and identify points of view or arguments through information sources.

- What are my print sources?

_____

_____

- What are my media sources?

_____

_____

- Who are my people sources?

_____

_____

- What primary and secondary sources might I use?

_____

_____

- What are my preliminary findings based on a review of existing sources?

_____

_____

3. Form a set of questions that can be answered by a specific set of data.

- What would be the results of _____?
- Who would benefit and by how much?

_____

_____

- Who would be harmed and by how much?

_____

_____

- My research questions: _____

_____

4. Gather evidence through research methods such as surveys, interviews, or information from primary and secondary source documents.

- What survey questions should I ask?

_____

_____

- What interview questions should I ask?

_____

_____

- What generalizations do secondary sources give?

_____

_____

- What data and evidence can I find in primary sources to support different sides of the issue?

_____

_____

5. **Manipulate and transform data so that they can be interpreted.**

- How can I summarize what I learned?

_____

_____

- Should I develop charts, diagrams, or graphs to represent my data?

_____

_____

6. Draw conclusions and make inferences.

- What do the data mean? How can I interpret what I found out?

_____

_____

- How do the data support my original point of view?

_____

_____

- How do they support other points of view?

_____

_____

- What conclusions can I make about the issue?

_____

_____

• What is my point of view now, based on the data?

_____

_____

7. Determine implications and consequences.

• What are the consequences of following the point of view that I support?

_____

_____

• Do I know enough or are there now new questions to be answered?

_____

_____

8. Communicate your findings. (Prepare an oral presentation for classmates based on notes and written report.)

• What are my purpose, issue, and point of view, and how will I explain them?

_____

_____

- What data will I use to support my point of view?

_____

_____

- How will I conclude my presentation?

_____

_____

Name: _____ Date: _____

Activity
11G

Topic Web

Directions: Brainstorm questions and possible sources for finding the answers to your questions.

What do I want to know?
(List questions)

What information resources would be best to pursue for each question?
(books, periodicals, people, Internet, CD-ROM)

Topic

What did I find out from each source?

What did I learn?

Name: _____ Date: _____

Vocabulary Web

Directions: Complete the Vocabulary Web for the word assigned to you.

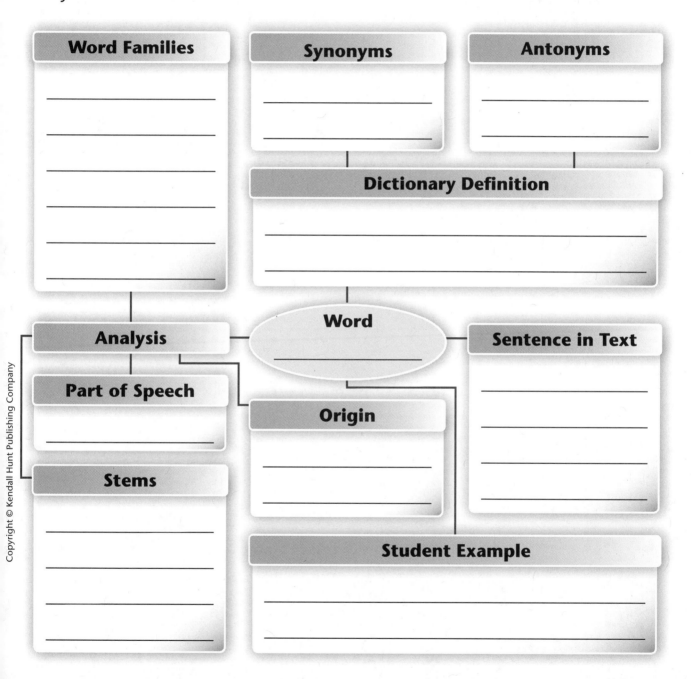

Word Families

Synonyms

Antonyms

Dictionary Definition

Word

Analysis

Part of Speech

Stems

Origin

Sentence in Text

Student Example

Copyright © Kendall Hunt Publishing Company

poem for
rodney

Nikki Giovanni

people always ask what
am i going to be
when i grow
up and i always
just think
i'd like to grow
up

"poem for rodney": From *Spin a Soft Black Song* by Nikki Giovanni. Copyright © 1971, 1985 by Nikki Giovanni. Reprinted by permission of Hill and Wang, a division of Farrar, Straus & Giroux, Inc.

Poem

Langston Hughes

I loved my friend.
He went away from me.
There's nothing more to say.
The poem ends,
Soft as it began—
I loved my friend.

Perfection

Felice Holman

Surely the turkey
is not pleased
to walk about with
knobbly knees,
his wattles
wobbling in the breeze.

And does the hog
enjoy his girth?
Or if the whim
were up to him
would he prefer
to be as slim
as I, perhaps,
and leave his bog?

From *I Hear You Smiling & Other Poems* by Felice Holman. Reprinted by permission of the author.

And so,
if I don't like myself
entirely,
I do suspect
the odd-necked goose
might trade with me,
if we could choose.
But then, would I
accept his neck
so I could fly?

Name: _____ Date: _____

Compare and Contrast
Poetry and Stories

Directions: Use the Venn diagram to compare and contrast poetry with stories in prose. Write ways they are alike in the middle part of the diagram and ways they are different in the outer parts. Include examples from the poems and stories you have read in this unit.

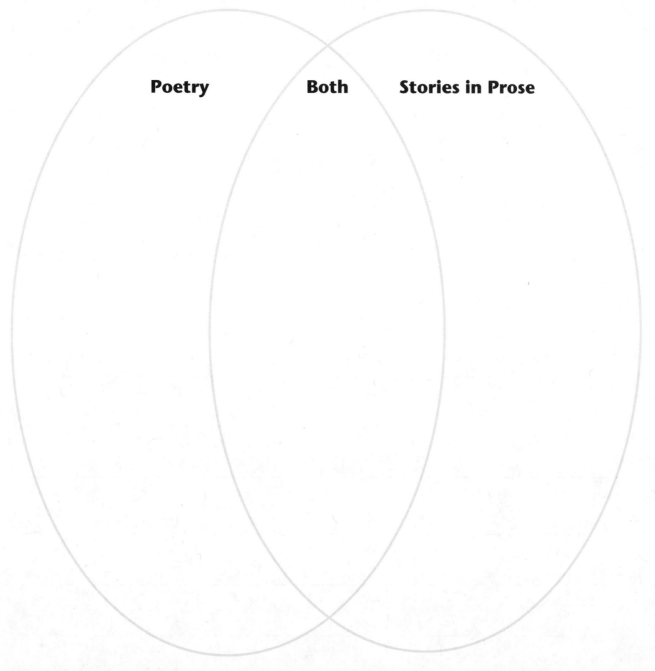

Poetry   **Both**   **Stories in Prose**

Name: _____ Date: _____

Activity
12B

Poetry Writing Prompts

Directions: Read the example, and then create your own prompts for writing poems.

Example prompt: Write a poem about "waiting." How do you feel when you have to wait? For what are you usually waiting?

1. _____

_____

_____

_____

_____

2. _____

_____

_____

_____

_____

3. _____

_____

_____

_____

_____

4. _____

_____

_____

_____

_____

Name: _____ Date: _____

Activity
12C

Writing About Change

Directions: Read the generalizations about change. Think about how they have been true in your own life. Choose one of the generalizations and circle it. Then list examples from your own life that show how the generalization has been true for you.

Change is linked to time.

Change is everywhere.

Change may be positive or negative.

Change may be perceived as orderly or random.

Change may happen naturally or be caused by people.

Examples:

_____

_____

_____

_____

_____

_____

Circle your three strongest examples. Then, write a persuasive paragraph showing that the generalization you chose is true. In the paragraph, state your opinion. Give your examples as evidence that the generalization is true. Explain your examples. Write a conclusion for your paragraph.

_____

_____

_____

_____

_____

_____

_____

_____

_____

_____

Activity
13A

Diamante Poem

What Is the Form of a Diamante Poem?

topic (noun)

two describing words (adjectives)

three action words (verbs or "-ing" words)

a four-word phrase telling a feeling about the topic

three action words (verbs or "-ing" words)

two describing words (adjectives)

ending word (noun, antonym for topic)

Two Diamante Poems

Anger	Ice
anger	ice
boiling, red-faced	smooth, solid
shouting, crying, pacing	gliding, skating, slipping
can't believe this happened	winter fun for skaters
talking, listening, talking	thawing, cracking, melting
calmer, quiet	thin, unsafe
acceptance	water

Name: _____ Date: _____

Activity
13B

Diamante Poem Ideas

Directions: In the left column, list topics for a diamante poem. In the right column, give the antonym for each topic. The topics and their antonyms should show how change is linked to time. See the two examples given below to help you get started. Remember, the topic will be the first word of the poem, and its antonym will be the last word.

Topic	Antonym
Night	Day
Summer	Winter

Name: _____ Date: _____

Diamante Poem

Directions: Choose a topic from Activity 13B. Write a diamante poem about the topic. Use Activity 13A as a guide. Remember to use the antonym of your topic as the last word of your poem. If you wish, write more poems on another sheet of paper.

Title: _____

_____

_____, _____

_____, _____, _____

_____

_____, _____, _____

_____, _____

_____

Name: _____ Date: _____

Activity
13D

Self-Review of Writing

Assignment: _____

Directions: For each sentence, circle the choice that best describes your writing. Then complete the two sentences.

1. My main idea is clear.

   Needs improvement   Satisfactory   Excellent

2. My details support the main idea.

   Needs improvement   Satisfactory   Excellent

3. My ideas flow smoothly and are in an order that makes sense.

   Needs improvement   Satisfactory   Excellent

4. The structure clearly follows the Hamburger Model (introduction, body, conclusion).

   Needs improvement   Satisfactory   Excellent

5. My vocabulary is rich and varied.

   Needs improvement   Satisfactory   Excellent

My writing is strong in these ways:

_____

_____

_____

My writing could be improved in these ways:

_____

_____

_____

Name: _____ Date: _____

Peer Review of Writing

Directions: For each sentence, circle the choice that best describes your partner's writing. Then complete the two sentences.

1. The main idea is clear.

   Needs improvement   Satisfactory   Excellent

2. The details support the main idea.

   Needs improvement   Satisfactory   Excellent

3. The ideas flow smoothly and are in an order that makes sense.

   Needs improvement   Satisfactory   Excellent

4. The structure clearly follows the Hamburger Model (introduction, body, conclusion).

   Needs improvement   Satisfactory   Excellent

5. The vocabulary is rich and varied.

   Needs improvement   Satisfactory   Excellent

The writing is strong in these ways:

_____

_____

_____

The writing could be improved in these ways:

_____

_____

_____

Diamante Poem on Day and Night

Directions: Write a diamante poem using the words *day* and *night*. You may begin the poem with either word. Use Activity 13A to remind you of the form of a diamante poem.

Title: _____

_____

_____ / _____

_____ / _____ / _____

_____

_____ / _____ / _____

_____ / _____

_____

Activity 14B

Creating Tessellations with Pattern Blocks

Directions: In the left column of the chart, list or draw each shape in your set of pattern blocks. Then decide if you can make a tessellation with each shape. Write *yes* or *no* in the right column. For each answer *yes*, draw the tessellation on a separate sheet of paper.

Shape	Can you make a tessellation with the shape?

Name: _____ Date: _____

Change Model

Directions: Find examples of change in *Free Fall*. Write two or more examples for each generalization.

Change is linked to time.

_____

_____

Change is everywhere.

_____

_____

Change

Change may be positive or negative.

_____

_____

Change may be perceived as orderly or random.

_____

_____

Change may happen naturally or may be caused by people.

_____

_____

Name: _____ Date: _____

Oral Presentation Evaluation Form

Speaker: _____ Assignment: _____

Directions: For items 1–8, circle the choice that describes the presentation. Then complete the two sentences.

Content and Organization

1. The speaker clearly stated the purpose of the story.

   Needs improvement   Satisfactory   Excellent

2. The speaker clearly described the sequence of events in the story.

   Needs improvement   Satisfactory   Excellent

3. The speaker clearly explained the main idea of the story.

   Needs improvement   Satisfactory   Excellent

4. The speaker clearly explained the ending of the story.

   Needs improvement   Satisfactory   Excellent

5. The ideas flowed smoothly and in an orderly way.

   Needs improvement   Satisfactory   Excellent

Delivery

6. The speaker made good eye contact with the audience.

   Needs improvement   Satisfactory   Excellent

7. The speaker spoke loudly enough for the entire audience to hear.

   Needs improvement   Satisfactory   Excellent

8. The speaker's words were clear and could be understood.

   Needs improvement   Satisfactory   Excellent

The best part of this presentation was:

_____

_____

_____

_____

A suggestion for improvement is:

_____

_____

_____

_____

Prepare for an Oral Presentation

Activity 15B

Directions: Write the title and the author of the story for your presentation at the top of the chart. Write the purpose of the story, the main events in the order they happen, the main idea, and the ending.

Title: _____ **Author:** _____
Purpose:
Main Events:
1. _____
2. _____
3. _____
4. _____
5. _____
Main Idea:
Ending:

The Ugly Duckling

Hans Christian Andersen

It was so beautiful out in the country. It was summer. The oats were still green, but the wheat was turning yellow. Down in the meadow the grass had been cut and made into haystacks; and there the storks walked on their long red legs talking Egyptian, because that was the language they had been taught by their mothers. The fields were enclosed by woods, and hidden among them were little lakes and pools. Yes, it certainly was lovely out there in the country!

The old castle, with its deep moat surrounding it, lay bathed in sunshine. Between the heavy walls and the edge of the moat there was a narrow strip of land covered by a whole forest of burdock plants. Their leaves were large and some of the stalks were so tall that a child could stand upright under them and imagine that he was in the middle of the wild and lonely woods. Here a duck had built her nest. While she sat waiting for the eggs to hatch, she felt a little sorry for herself because it was taking so long and hardly anybody came to visit her. The other ducks preferred swimming in the moat to sitting under a dock leaf and gossiping.

Finally the eggs began to crack. "Peep … Peep," they said one after another. The egg yolks had become alive and were sticking out their heads.

"Quack … Quack …" said their mother. "Look around you." And the ducklings did; they glanced at the green world about them, and that was what their mother wanted them to do, for green was good for their eyes.

"How big the world is!" piped the little ones, for they had much more space to move around in now than they had had inside the egg.

"Do you think that this is the whole world?" quacked their mother. "The world is much larger than this. It stretches as far as the minister's wheat fields, though I have not been there. … Are you all here?" The duck got up and turned around to look at the nest. "Oh no, the biggest egg hasn't hatched yet; and I'm so tired of sitting here! I wonder how long it will take?" she wailed, and sat down again.

"What's new?" asked an old duck who had come visiting.

"One of the eggs is taking so long," complained the mother duck. "It won't crack. But take a look at the others. They are the sweetest little ducklings you have ever seen; and every one of them looks exactly like their father. That scoundrel hasn't come to visit me once."

"Let me look at the egg that won't hatch," demanded the old duck. "I am sure that it's a turkey egg! I was fooled that way once. You can't imagine what it's like. Turkeys are afraid of the water. I couldn't get them to go into it. I quacked and I nipped them, but nothing helped. Let me see that egg! … Yes, it's a turkey egg. Just let it lie there. You go and teach your young ones how to swim, that's my advice."

"I have sat on it so long that I suppose I can sit a little longer, at least until they get the hay in," replied the mother duck.

"Suit yourself," said the older duck, and went on.

At last the big egg cracked too. "Peep … Peep," said the young one, and tumbled out. He was big and very ugly.

The mother duck looked at him. "He's awfully big for his age," she said. "He doesn't look like any of the others. I wonder if he could be a turkey? Well, we shall soon see. Into the water he will go, even if I have to kick him to make him do it."

The next day the weather was gloriously beautiful. The sun shone on the forest of burdock plants. The mother duck took her whole brood to the moat. "Quack … Quack …" she ordered.

One after another, the little ducklings plunged into the water. For a moment their heads disappeared, but then they popped up again and the little ones floated like so many corks. Their legs knew what to do without being told. All of the new brood swam very nicely, even the ugly one.

"He is no turkey," mumbled the mother. "See how beautifully he uses his legs and how straight he holds his neck. He is my own child and, when you look closely at him, he's quite handsome. Quack! Quack! Follow me and I'll take you to the henyard and introduce you to everyone. But stay close to me, so that no one steps on you, and look out for the cat."

They heard an awful noise when they arrived at the henyard. Two families of ducks had gotten into a fight over the head of an eel. Neither of them got it, for it was swiped by the cat.

"That is the way of the world," said the mother duck, and licked her bill. She would have liked to have had the eel's head herself. "Walk nicely," she admonished them. "And remember to bow to the old duck over there. She has Spanish blood in her veins and is the most aristocratic fowl here. That is why she is so fat and has a red rag tied around one of her legs. That is the highest mark of distinction a duck can be given. It means so much that she will never be done away with; and all the other fowl and the human beings know who she is. Quack! Quack! … Don't walk, waddle like well-brought-up ducklings. Keep your legs far apart, just as your mother and father have always done. Bow your heads and say, 'Quack!'" And that was what the little ducklings did.

Other ducks gathered about them and said loudly, "What do we want that gang here for? Aren't there enough of us already? Pooh! Look how ugly one of them is! He's the last straw!" And one of the ducks flew over and bit the ugly duckling on the neck.

"Leave him alone!" shouted the mother. "He hasn't done anyone any harm."

"He's big and he doesn't look like everybody else!" replied the duck who had bitten him. "And that's reason enough to beat him."

"Very good-looking children you have," remarked the duck with the red rag around one of her legs. "All of them are beautiful except one. He didn't turn out very well. I wish you could make him over again."

"That's not possible, Your Grace," answered the mother duck. "He may not be handsome, but he has a good character and swims as well as the others, if not a little better. Perhaps he will grow handsomer as he grows older and becomes a bit smaller. He was in the egg too long, and that is why he doesn't have the right shape." She smoothed his neck for a moment and then added, "Besides, he's a drake; and it doesn't matter so much what he looks like. He is strong and I am sure he will be able to take care of himself."

"Well, the others are nice," said the old duck. "Make yourself at home, and if you should find an eel's head, you may bring it to me."

And they were "at home."

The poor little duckling, who had been the last to hatch and was so ugly, was bitten and pushed and made fun of both by the hens and by the other ducks. The turkey cock (who had been born with spurs on, and therefore thought he was an emperor) rustled his feathers as if he were a full-rigged ship under sail, and strutted up to the duckling. He gobbled so loudly at him that his own face got all red.

The poor little duckling did not know where to turn. How he grieved over his own ugliness, and how sad he was! The poor creature was mocked and laughed at by the whole henyard.

That was the first day; and each day that followed was worse than the one before. The poor duckling was chased and mistreated by everyone, even his own sisters and brothers, who quacked again and again, "If only the cat would get you, you ugly thing!"

Even his mother said, "I wish you were far away." The other ducks bit him and the hens pecked at him. The little girl who came to feed the fowls kicked him.

At last the duckling ran away. He flew over the tops of the bushes, frightening all the little birds so that they flew up into the air. "They, too, think I am ugly," thought the duckling, and closed his eyes—but he kept on running.

Finally he came to a great swamp where wild ducks lived; and here he stayed for the night, for he was too tired to go any farther.

In the morning he was discovered by the wild ducks. They looked at him and one of them asked, "What kind of bird are you?"

The ugly duckling bowed in all directions, for he was trying to be as polite as he knew how.

"You are ugly," said the wild ducks, "but that is no concern of ours, as long as you don't try to marry into our family."

The poor duckling wasn't thinking of marriage. All he wanted was to be allowed to swim among the reeds and drink a little water when he was thirsty.

He spent two days in the swamp; then two wild geese came—or rather, two wild ganders, for they were drakes. They had been hatched not long ago; therefore they were both frank and bold.

"Listen, comrade," they said. "You are so ugly that we like you. Do you want to migrate with us? Not far from here there is marsh where some beautiful wild geese live. They are all lovely maidens, and you are so ugly that you may seek your fortune among them. Come along."

"Bang! Bang!" Two shots were heard and both ganders fell down dead among the reeds, and the water turned red from their blood.

"Bang! Bang!" Again came the sound of shots, and a flock of wild geese flew up.

The whole swamp was surrounded by hunters; from every direction came the awful noise. Some of the hunters had hidden behind bushes or among the reeds, but others screened from sight by the leaves, sat on the long, low branches of the trees that stretched out over the swamp. The blue smoke from the guns lay like a fog over the water and among the trees. Dogs came splashing through the marsh, and they bent and broke the reeds.

The poor little duckling was terrified. He was about to tuck his head under his wing in order to hide when he saw a big dog peering at him through the reeds. The dog's tongue hung out of its mouth and its eyes glistened evilly. It bared its teeth. Splash! It turned away without touching the duckling.

"Oh, thank God!" he sighed. "I am so ugly that even the dog doesn't want to bite me."

The little duckling lay as still as he could while the shots whistled through the reeds. Not until the middle of the afternoon did the shooting stop; but the poor little duckling was still so frightened that he waited several hours longer before taking his head out from under his wing. Then he ran as quickly as he could out of the swamp. Across the fields and the meadows he went, but a wind had come up and he found it hard to make his way against it.

Towards evening he came upon a poor little hut. It was so wretchedly crooked that it looked as if it couldn't make up its mind which way to fall and that was why it was still standing. The wind was blowing so hard that the poor little duckling had to sit down in order not to be blown away. Suddenly he noticed that the door was off its hinges, making a crack, and he squeezed himself through it and was inside.

An old woman lived in the hut with her cat and her hen. The cat was called Sonny and could both arch his back and purr. Oh yes, it could also make sparks if you rubbed its fur the wrong way. The hen had very short legs and that was why it was called Cluck Lowlegs. But she was good at laying eggs, and the old woman loved her as if she were her own child.

In the morning the hen and the cat discovered the duckling. The cat meowed and the hen clucked.

"What is going on?" asked the old woman, and looked around. She couldn't see very well, and when she found the duckling she thought it was a fat, full-grown duck. "What a fine catch!" she exclaimed. "Now we shall have duck eggs, unless it's a drake. We'll give it a try."

So the duckling was allowed to stay for three weeks on probation, but he laid no eggs. The cat was the master of the house and the hen the mistress. They always referred to themselves as "we and the world," for they thought that they were half the world—and the better half at that. The duckling thought that he should be allowed to have a different opinion, but the hen did not agree.

"Can you lay eggs?" she demanded.

"No," answered the duckling.

"Then keep your mouth shut."

And the cat asked, "Can you arch your back? Can you purr? Can you make sparks?"

"No."

"Well in that case, you have no right to have an opinion when sensible people are talking."

The duckling was sitting in a corner and was in a bad mood. Suddenly he recalled how lovely it could be outside in the fresh air when the sun shone: a great longing to be floating in the water came over the duckling, and he could not help talking about it.

"What is the matter with you?" asked the hen as soon as she had heard what he had to say. "You have nothing to do, that's why you get ideas like that. Lay eggs or purr, and such notions will disappear."

"You have no idea how delightful it is to float in the water and to dive down to the bottom of the lake and get your head wet," said the duckling.

"Yes, that certainly does sound amusing," said the hen. "You must have gone mad. Ask the cat—he is the most intelligent being I know—ask him whether he likes to swim or dive down to the bottom of a lake. Don't take my word for anything … ask the old woman who is the cleverest person in the world; ask her whether she likes to float and get her head all wet."

"You don't understand me!" wailed the duckling.

"And if I don't understand you, who will? I hope you don't think that you are wiser than the cat or the old woman—not to mention myself. Don't give yourself airs! Thank your Creator for all He has done for you. Aren't you sitting in a warm room, where you can hear intelligent conversation that you could learn something from?

While you, yourself, do nothing but say a lot of nonsense and aren't the least bit amusing! Believe me, that's the truth, no matter how unpleasant it is. Now get to work: lay some eggs, or learn to purr and arch your back."

"I think I'll go out into the wide world," replied the duckling.

"Go right ahead!" said the hen.

And the duckling left. He found a lake where he could float in the water and dive to the bottom. There were other ducks, but they ignored him because he was so ugly.

Autumn came and the leaves turned yellow and brown, then they fell from the trees. The wind caught them and made them dance. The clouds were heavy with hail and snow. A raven sat on a fence and screeched, "Ach! Ach!" because it was so cold. When just thinking of how cold it was is enough to make one shiver, what a terrible time the duckling must have had.

One evening just as the sun was setting gloriously, a flock of beautiful birds came out from among the rushes. Their feathers were so white that they glistened; and they had long, graceful necks. They were swans. They made a very loud cry, then they spread their powerful wings. They were flying south to a warmer climate, where the lakes were not frozen in the winter. Higher and higher they circled. The ugly duckling turned round and round in the water like a wheel and stretched his neck up toward the sky; he felt a strange longing. He screeched so piercingly that he frightened himself.

Oh, he would never forget those beautiful birds, those happy birds. When they were out of sight the duckling dived down under the water to the bottom of the lake; and when he came up again he was beside himself. He did not know the name of those birds or where they were going, and yet he felt he loved them as he had never loved any other creatures. He did not envy them. It did not even occur to him to wish that he were so handsome himself. He would have been happy if the other ducks had let him stay in the henyard. That poor, ugly bird!

The weather grew colder and colder. The duckling had to swim round and round in the water, to keep just a little space for himself that wasn't frozen. Each night the hole became smaller and smaller. On all sides of him, the ice creaked and groaned. The little duckling had to keep his feet constantly in motion so that the last bit of open water wouldn't become ice. At last he was too tired to swim any more. He sat still. The ice closed in around him and he was frozen fast.

Early the next morning a farmer saw him and with his clogs broke the ice to free the duckling. The man put the bird under his arm and took it home to his wife, who brought the duckling back to life.

The children wanted to play with him. But the duckling was afraid they were going to hurt him, so he flapped his wings and flew right into the milk pail. From there he flew into a big bowl of butter and then into a barrel of flour. What a sight he was!

The farmer's wife yelled and chased him with a poker. The children laughed and almost fell on top of each other trying to catch him; and how they screamed! Luckily for the duckling, the door was open. He got out of the house and found a hiding place beneath some bushes, in the newly fallen snow; and there he lay so still as though there were hardly any life left in him.

It would be too horrible to tell of all the hardship and suffering the duckling experienced that long winter. It is enough to know that he did survive. When again the sun began to shine warmly and the larks began to sing, the duckling was lying among the reeds in the swamp. Spring had come!

He spread out his wings to fly. How strong and powerful they were! Before he knew it he was far from the swamp and flying above a beautiful garden. The apple trees were blooming and the lilac bushes stretched their flower-covered branches over the water of a winding canal. Everything was so beautiful—so fresh and green. Out of a forest of rushes came three swans. They ruffled their feathers and floated so lightly on the water. The ugly duckling recognized the birds and felt again that strange sadness come over him.

"I shall fly over to them, those royal birds! And they can hack me to death because I, who am so ugly, dare to approach them! What difference does it make? It is better to be killed by them than to be bitten by the other ducks, and pecked by the hens, and kicked by the girl who tends the henyard, or to suffer through the winter."

He lighted on the water and swam towards the magnificent swans. When they saw him they ruffled their feathers and started to swim in his direction. They were coming to meet him.

"Kill me," whispered the poor creature and bent his head calmly as he waited for death. But what was that he saw in the water? It was his own reflection, and he was no longer an awkward, clumsy, grey bird, so ungainly and so ugly. He was a swan!

It does not matter that one has been born in the henyard as long as one has lain in a swan's egg.

He was thankful that he had known so much want and gone through so much suffering, for it made him appreciate his present happiness and the loveliness of everything about him all the more. The swans made a circle around him and caressed him with their beaks.

Some children came out into the garden. They had brought bread with them to feed the swans. The youngest child shouted, "Look, there's a new one!" All the children joyfully clapped their hands, and they ran to tell their parents.

Cake and bread were cast on the water for the swans. Everyone agreed that the new swan was the most beautiful of them all. The older swans bowed toward him.

He felt so shy that he hid his head beneath his wing. He was too happy, but not proud, for a kind heart can never be proud. He thought of the time when he had been mocked and persecuted. And now everyone said that he was the most beautiful of the most beautiful birds. And the lilac bushes stretched their branches right down to the water for him. The sun shone so warm and brightly. He ruffled his feathers and raised his slender neck while out of the joy in his heart, he thought, "Such happiness I did not dream of when I was the ugly duckling."

Name: _____ Date: _____

 **Activity**
16A
What Would You Change?

Directions: Think of two things you would like to change about yourself. Think of two things you would not like to change about yourself. Write your responses in the chart.

Things I Would Like to Change	Things I Would Not Like to Change
1. _____ _____ _____ _____	1. _____ _____ _____ _____
2. _____ _____ _____ _____	2. _____ _____ _____ _____

Activity
16B

Literature Web

Directions: Complete the Literature Web for "The Ugly Duckling."

Key Words	Feelings
_____	_____
_____	_____
_____	_____
_____	_____

Title
_____
_____
_____

Ideas	Images or Symbols
_____	_____
_____	_____
_____	_____
_____	_____

Name: _____ Date: _____

Activity
16C

Concept Web: Pride

Directions: Create a Concept Web about pride.

Pride

Name: _____ Date: _____

Vocabulary Web

Directions: Complete the Vocabulary Web for the word assigned to you.

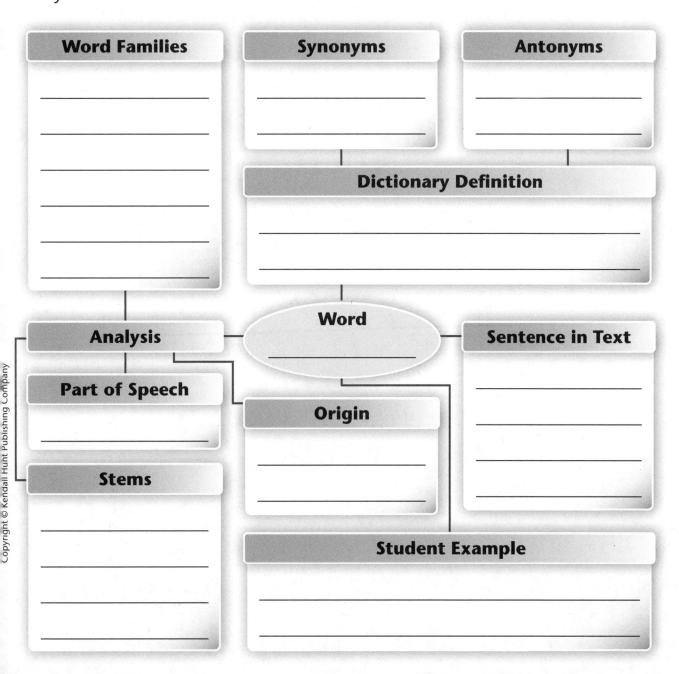

Word Families	Synonyms	Antonyms

Dictionary Definition

Word

Analysis

Part of Speech

Origin

Sentence in Text

Stems

Student Example

Biographical Sketch: Hans Christian Andersen

Activity
17A

Directions: Read this biographical sketch of Hans Christian Anderson. Think about ways in which his biography is similar to and different from the story of "The Ugly Duckling." You may make notes in the space below each paragraph.

Hans Christian Anderson is famous for writing many enchanting fairy tales, including "The Ugly Duckling" and "The Emperor's New Clothes." He was born in 1805 in Odense, on the island of Fyn, in Denmark. He was the only child in a poor family. His father, a cobbler, died when he was 11, and his mother took a job as a washerwoman, leaving Hans to dream and fantasize alone.

_____

_____

_____

In school, the other children made fun of Andersen's awkwardness and his large hands and feet. After his father's death, he stopped going to school. Instead, he stayed at home, reading as many books as he could find and creating puppets and paper cutouts. His own make-believe games, combined with the fantastic stories his mother told him as a child, laid the foundation for the fairy tales he wrote as an adult.

_____

_____

_____

At the age of 14, Andersen left home for Copenhagen in hopes of becoming an opera singer and dancer. Because of his poor voice and lanky, awkward body, his musical dream was never fulfilled. However, he met several friends who encouraged his writing and education and eventually made it possible for him to go to a university. He did not like the university, where he studied for six years. Even though he towered over the younger students, both the students and teachers bullied him.

_____

_____

_____

As an adult, Andersen earned his living by writing. In 1829 he wrote his first successful book. It earned him enough money that he could travel around Europe. He then wrote about his travels in a novel. In 1835 he published a book of fairy tales. He continued to write novels, plays, and travel sketches, but he also began a second and third series of fairy tales. His stories were translated into English, and Andersen became a celebrity wherever he traveled. Children accepted and loved him, and they understood him better than grownups. Andersen never married. He continued to write fairy tales until he died in 1875 at the age of 70. During his lifetime he wrote 168 fairy tales.

_____

_____

_____

Compare and Contrast an Author and His Work

Activity 17B

Directions: Use the Venn diagram to compare and contrast the biography of Hans Christian Andersen with the story of "The Ugly Duckling." Write ways they are alike in the middle part of the diagram and ways they are different in the outer parts.

Hans Christian Andersen's Life

Both

The Ugly Duckling's Story

Name: _____ Date: _____

Activity
17C

Interview Questions

Directions: Imagine interviewing a parent or another adult family member. Think about questions you would ask to find out about the changes in this person's life. Write the questions in the chart.

Possible Interview Questions
1. _____ _____
2. _____ _____
3. _____ _____
4. _____ _____
5. _____ _____

Now add questions from your class discussion. Then read all the questions you wrote. Circle the five questions you plan to use in your interview.

6. _____

_____

7. _____

_____

8. _____

_____

9. _____

_____

10. _____

_____

Name: _____ Date: _____

Activity
17D

Change Chart

Directions: Choose a person who has done something special in the arts or science. Read about this person. Use the chart to take notes about things that did and did not change in the person's life.

Person: _____ Career: _____	
Things that changed:	**Things that did not change:**

Now write a paragraph explaining how the events and changes in the person's life led the person choosing his or her career.

_____

_____

_____

_____

_____

_____

_____

_____

_____

_____

_____

Literature Web

Directions: Complete the Literature Web for *Bringing the Rain to Kapiti Plain.*

Key Words	Feelings
_____	_____
_____	_____
_____	_____
_____	_____

Title

_____
_____
_____

Ideas	Images or Symbols
_____	_____
_____	_____
_____	_____
_____	_____

Name: _____ Date: _____

Activity
18B

Compare and
Contrast Two Stories

Directions: Use the Venn diagram to compare and contrast *Bringing the Rain to Kapiti Plain* with *Rain Player*. Write ways they are alike in the middle part of the diagram and ways they are different in the outer parts.

Bringing the Rain to Kapiti Plain

Both

Rain Player

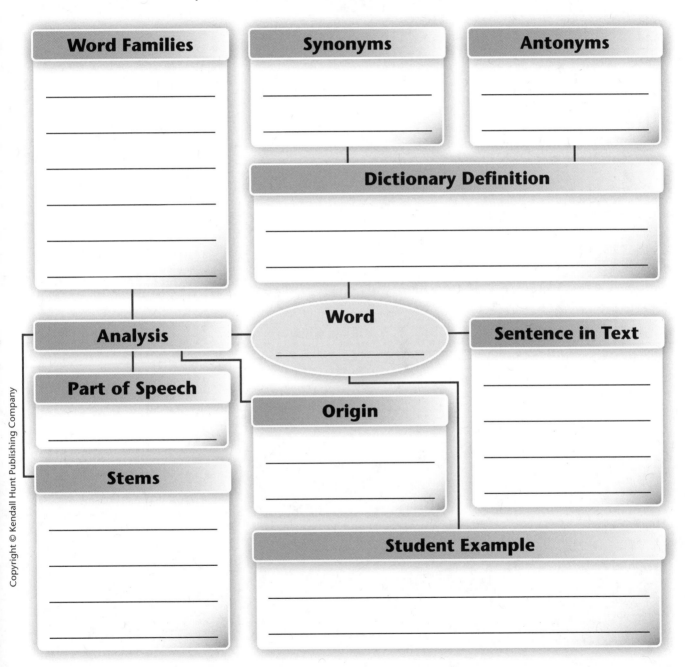

Activity 18C

Vocabulary Web

Directions: Complete the Vocabulary Web for the word "migrated."

Word Families

_____
_____
_____
_____
_____
_____

Synonyms

_____
_____

Antonyms

_____
_____

Dictionary Definition

_____
_____

Analysis

Word

_____

Sentence in Text

_____
_____
_____

Part of Speech

_____

Origin

_____
_____

Stems

_____
_____

Student Example

_____
_____

Ozymandias

Percy Shelley

I met a traveller from an antique land
Who said: Two vast and trunkless legs of stone
Stand in the desert. Near them on the sand,
Half sunk, a shatter'd visage lies, whose frown
And wrinkled lip and sneer of cold command
Tell that its sculptor well those passions read
Which yet survive, stamp'd on these lifeless things,
The hand that mock'd them and the heart that fed.
And on the pedestal these words appear:
"My name is Ozymandias, king of kings:
Look on my works, ye Mighty, and despair!"
Nothing beside remains. Round the decay
Of that colossal wreck, boundless and bare,
The lone and level sands stretch far away.

Name: _____ Date: _____

 **Activity**
19A

Vocabulary Web

Directions: Complete the Vocabulary Web for the word assigned to you.

Word Families	Synonyms	Antonyms
_____	_____	_____
_____	_____	_____
_____		
_____		
_____		

Dictionary Definition
_____
_____

Word
_____

Analysis

Part of Speech
_____

Stems
_____
_____
_____

Origin
_____
_____

Sentence in Text
_____
_____
_____

Student Example
_____
_____

Literature Web

Directions: Complete the Literature Web for "Ozymandias."

Key Words	**Feelings**
_____	_____
_____	_____
_____	_____
_____	_____

Title

_____

_____

_____

Ideas	**Images or Symbols**
_____	_____
_____	_____
_____	_____
_____	_____

Name: _____ Date: _____

Activity
19C

Illustrate the Poem

Directions: In the space, draw the broken statue in the desert described in "Ozymandias."

Copyright © Kendall Hunt Publishing Company

Name: _____ Date: _____

Compare and Contrast
Two Landscapes

Directions: Use the Venn diagram to compare the landscape in *Bringing the Rain to Kapiti Plain* with the landscape described in "Ozymandias."

Kenyan Landscape

from *Bringing the Rain to Kapiti Plain*

Both

Egyptian Landscape

from "Ozymandias"

Name: _____ Date: _____

Hamburger Model for Persuasive Writing

Directions: Think about what you feel is the best way to preserve memories, based on your research. Use the Hamburger Model to organize the reasons. Then write a persuasive paper to respond to the prompt, "What is the best way to preserve memories?"

Introduction
(State your opinion.)

_____
_____

Elaboration	**Elaboration**	**Elaboration**
_____	_____	_____
_____	_____	_____

Reason	**Reason**	**Reason**
_____	_____	_____
_____	_____	_____

Elaboration	**Elaboration**	**Elaboration**
_____	_____	_____
_____	_____	_____

Conclusion

_____
_____

Name: _____ Date: _____

 **Activity 20B**

Standards of Reasoning

Directions: Use the questions to review the argument in your persuasive paper. Note the improvements that you should make.

1. Are enough reasons given to make the argument convincing? Note any improvements that could be made.

_____

_____

_____

2. Is the supporting evidence factual and correct? Note any improvements that could be made.

_____

_____

_____

3. Are the reasons clear? Are they explained thoroughly, or is more information needed? Note any improvements that could be made.

_____

_____

_____

4. Are the reasons and evidence specific, or are they general and vague? Note any improvements that could be made.

_____

_____

_____

5. Are the reasons strong and important? Note any improvements that could be made.

_____

_____

_____

6. Is the argument logical? Do the sentences seem to go together, and does their order make sense? Note any improvements that could be made.

_____

_____

_____

Name: _____ Date: _____

Activity
20C

Self-Review of Writing

Directions: For each sentence, circle the choice that best describes your writing. Then complete the two sentences.

1. My main idea is clear.

Needs improvement   Satisfactory   Excellent

2. My details support the main idea.

Needs improvement   Satisfactory   Excellent

3. My ideas flow smoothly and are in an order that makes sense.

Needs improvement   Satisfactory   Excellent

4. The structure clearly follows the Hamburger Model (introduction, body, conclusion).

Needs improvement   Satisfactory   Excellent

5. My vocabulary is rich and varied.

Needs improvement   Satisfactory   Excellent

My writing is strong in these ways:

_____

_____

_____

My writing could be improved in these ways:

_____

_____

_____

Name: _____ Date: _____

Activity
20D
Peer Review of Writing

Directions: For each sentence, circle the choice that best describes your writing. Then complete the two sentences.

1. The main idea is clear.

   Needs improvement   Satisfactory   Excellent

2. The details support the main idea.

   Needs improvement   Satisfactory   Excellent

3. The ideas flow smoothly and are in an order that makes sense.

   Needs improvement   Satisfactory   Excellent

4. The structure clearly follows the Hamburger Model (introduction, body, conclusion).

   Needs improvement   Satisfactory   Excellent

5. The vocabulary is rich and varied.

   Needs improvement   Satisfactory   Excellent

The writing is strong in these ways:

_____

_____

_____

The writing could be improved in these ways:

_____

_____

_____

**Activity
21A**

Literature Web

Directions: Complete the Literature Web for *Sachiko Means Happiness*.

Key Words
_____
_____
_____
_____

Feelings
_____
_____
_____
_____

Title
_____
_____
_____

Ideas
_____
_____
_____
_____

Images or Symbols
_____
_____
_____
_____

Name: _____ Date: _____

 **Activity**
21B

Compare Artwork from Japan and Kenya

Directions: Look at the images of artwork from Japan and Kenya. List the ways they are similar. List the ways they are different.

How are they similar?	How are they different?

Vocabulary Web

Directions: Complete the Vocabulary Web for the word assigned to you.

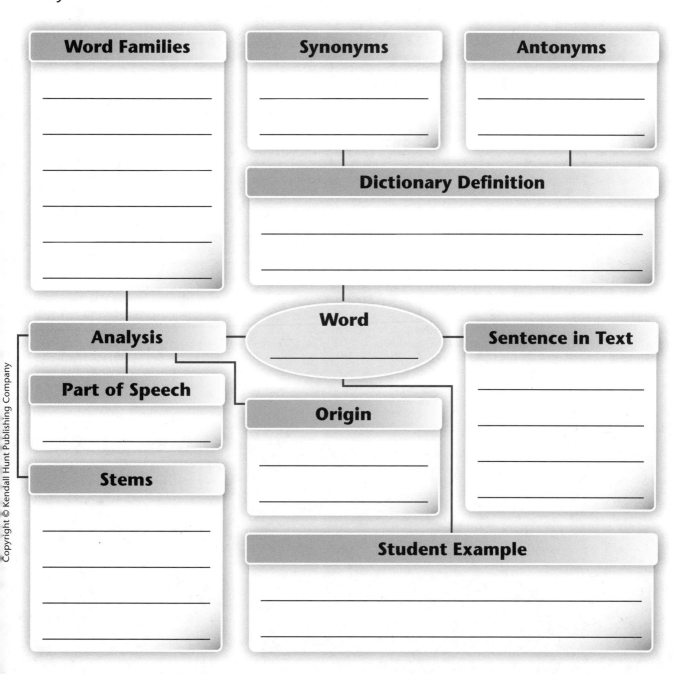

Name: _____ Date: _____

Oral Presentation Evaluation Form

Speaker: _____ Assignment: _____

Directions: For items 1–10, circle the choice that describes the presentation. Then complete the two sentences.

Content

1. The purpose of the presentation was clear.

   Needs improvement   Satisfactory   Excellent

2. The speaker included details that supported the main idea.

   Needs improvement   Satisfactory   Excellent

3. The speaker showed knowledge of the subject.

   Needs improvement   Satisfactory   Excellent

4. The speaker used vocabulary that was rich and varied.

   Needs improvement   Satisfactory   Excellent

Organization

5. The speech followed the Hamburger Model, with a clear introduction, body, and conclusion.

   Needs improvement   Satisfactory   Excellent

6. The ideas flowed smoothly and in an orderly way.

   Needs improvement   Satisfactory   Excellent

7. The speaker closed the presentation with a strong, interesting idea that restated the purpose.

Needs improvement   Satisfactory   Excellent

Delivery

8. The speaker made good eye contact with the audience.

Needs improvement   Satisfactory   Excellent

9. The speaker spoke loudly enough for the entire audience to hear.

Needs improvement   Satisfactory   Excellent

10. The speaker's words were clear and could be understood.

Needs improvement   Satisfactory   Excellent

The best part of this presentation was:

_____

_____

_____

A suggestion for improvement is:

_____

_____

_____

Name: _____ Date: _____

Plan an Oral Presentation

Directions: Choose a character from one of the stories in this unit. Answer the questions about this character. Then use your answers to the questions to plan a short oral presentation. In your presentation, you will describe the character and how he or she did or did not change in the story. You will also explain why you find this character interesting.

1. Who is the character, and in what story does the character appear?

_____

_____

_____

_____

_____

2. How would you describe the character?

_____

_____

_____

_____

_____

3. Does the character change in the story? If so, how? If the character does not change, describe what does not change about the character.

_____

_____

_____

_____

4. Why do you find the character interesting?

_____

_____

_____

_____

The Green Man

Gail E. Haley

Claude was the only son of Squire Archibald. He was arrogant, vain, and selfish. He spent most of his time hunting, hawking, and riding about the countryside in his fine clothes.

One evening Claude rode into the village, and after ordering a lavish meal at The Mermaid and Bush, he sat watching the bustle of village life.

"Look at those ignorant peasants putting food out for the Green Man when they can barely feed their own children."

"They are grateful, Master Claude," replied the landlord. "For the Green Man keeps their animals healthy. He protects their children if they stray into the forest. Without him, the crops would not grow, nor the seasons turn in their course."

"Rubbish! Those are just silly tales. There is no Green Man!"

"Mind your tongue, sir," chided the landlord. "Terrible things can happen to those who make fun of old beliefs."

Some days afterward, Claude set out for a day's hunting. He never hunted on foot; he preferred to shoot from horseback. His men and dogs had gone ahead as beaters to drive the game toward him, but nothing was happening, and Claude grew tired of waiting. He rode deeper into the forest.

"Those beaters are incompetent. I haven't seen an animal all day!" he grumbled.

Soon Claude was hopelessly lost. It was hot, and his clothes felt heavy, when through the trees he saw a shady pond. Tethering his horse to a tree, he stripped off his clothes and dived into the cool water. He did not see a thin, bony hand reaching out of the bushes.

Claude came out of the water refreshed and hungry, but on the bank he found nothing but a coil of rope.

Claude tied some leafy branches around his waist with the rope. Then he ate some of the strawberries that were growing on the bank. Feeling better, he chose a stout branch as a walking stick and set off to find his way home. But as the day drew to a close, Claude realized he would have to spend the night in the forest.

Peering about in the gloom, he saw before him the entrance to a large cave and felt his way inside. As he grew accustomed to the dark, Claude realized that he was not alone. There seemed to be something with glittering eyes and sharp horns near the mouth of the cave.

"Stay back! I'm armed!" Claude shouted. But the creature came no closer. Then something moved near the back of the cave. Claude clutched his stick for protection and drew his legs up onto a ledge. He lay there until, exhausted, he fell asleep.

When Claude woke it was morning and a little nanny goat was standing before him, tossing her head. He laughed with relief. It must have been she who had been at the back of the cave in the night.

Claude looked around. A young rooster was pecking busily near a nest full of eggs. A clay jug and a stone ax hung on the wall above Claude's head. Several rough baskets stood on the floor, and there was ash from a recent fire.

"This is someone's home," thought Claude. "Perhaps I should feed the animals." He gave the hens some grain which he found in a bowl and picked some fresh grass for the goat as a special treat. Then he helped himself to goat's milk and eggs.

The goat nuzzled his hand, and he scratched her behind the ears. She frisked about and followed him when he set off to explore.

Not far away, Claude found a bees' nest in a tree, its honeycomb shining from inside the hollow trunk. Covering his body with mud to protect himself from stings, he climbed up to collect some honey.

Just then, a party of his father's men broke through the trees, blowing their horns and hallooing for him.

Journeys and Destinations · Lesson 23 · "The Green Man"

"They'll think I've gone mad, if they see me sitting in a tree covered with mud," thought Claude. "I can't let them see me without my clothes and my boots. I would be disgraced!"

So he let the party pass without revealing himself. Then he climbed down from the tree and crept back to the cave, followed all the time by the goat.

"I'll borrow something to cover myself from the owner of the cave when he returns, and then I'll set off for home again," Claude said to his new friend, the goat. But time passed, and no one came. Claude lived on in the cave, growing leaner and stronger every day.

As the warm days went by, Claude forgot altogether about clothes. He nearly forgot that he was Claude, the Squire's son. He became Milker-of-the-Goat, Feeder-of-the-Hens, Friend-of-All- Wild-Animals. The forest creatures were not afraid of him. He fed them, talked to them, and spent hours watching them hunt and play.

As the berries, fruits, and nuts ripened, Claude became Gatherer-and-Preserver. When the grain was harvested in distant fields, he became Gleaner, venturing out at night to gather the leftovers for himself and his animals.

Claude was enjoying his new life. Even the sun and the moon seemed to smile upon him.

One morning, after a heavy rainstorm, Claude heard a frantic bellow coming from the direction of the river. He hurried there see what was wrong, and found a cow who had been separated from her calf. They had taken shelter from the rain in a hilltop thicket, and as the water rose the river had surrounded them, turning the hillock into an island. The terrified calf would not follow its mother through the swirling current, and the cow was mooing loudly for help.

Claude waded across the water, picked up the calf, and carried it to its mother. Gratefully, the cow licked his hand and then led her calf away through the forest toward the safety of the farmyard.

As the days grew colder, Claude added more ivy leaves to his costume. He tucked strips of moss and lichen between them to keep out the cold. He pounded birch bark to make it soft, and sewed pieces together to make a curtain for the mouth of the cave. After several attempts he even succeeded in making himself some birch-bark boots.

He built a fireplace near the entrance. He had found stones the right size and shape to make a mortar and a pestle, and each day he ground grain or nuts or acorns into flour. The smell of baking bread filled the air. A family of hedgehogs moved in.

The cave was now well stocked with food. Strings of mushrooms, parsnips, wild onions, and herbs hung on drying poles. Claude made slings for the fruit and vegetables he had gathered. He formed barrels out of bark to hold apples and roots. Baskets of nuts, grain, and seeds were stored on a shelf above his mossy bed.

One day when Claude was out gathering acorns, he encountered a fierce wild boar threatening two small children from the village.

"Don't be such a selfish swine!" Claude spoke firmly to the boar. "There are enough acorns for everyone. Go away and let the children have their share."

The boar snorted defiantly but turned and trotted back into the forest.

"There, there, don't cry. The old boar is gone now," Claude comforted the children.

The girl looked up through her tears at the tall, sunburned man. He seemed as ancient, green, and moss-covered as the oak tree that towered above them.

"Are you the Green Man?" she asked in a whisper.

Claude looked down in surprise. Warm sunshine caressed his hair. A gentle breeze rippled his leafy costume. His feet felt as if they were rooted in the earth.

"Yes," Claude answered her at last. "I am the Green Man."

He helped the children to gather up their acorns and filled their basket to the brim. Then he led them safely to the edge of the forest.

When winter came, at night Claude visited the nearby sleeping villages. He helped himself to some of the food put out for him but always left some for the hungry, prowling animals. At times he felt lonely as he walked through the deserted streets, looking into the windows of the cozy houses. He was homesick for his own village and his family. But he returned each night to his cave and his animals. He was needed now in the forest.

Winter passed and spring was on its way. The smell of budding leaves, warm earth, and growing things filled the air. The day went by, and when he knew that the strawberries would be ripening by the pond, Claude went to pick them.

A man was splashing in the water. A fine suit of clothing lay on the bank and a handsome horse was tethered nearby.

Claude quietly took off his leaves and put on the clothes. He found shears and a glass in the horse's saddlebag, so he cut his long hair and trimmed his beard. Then he rode through the forest until he found his own home.

His mother and father were amazed and delighted to see him. Everyone thought he had been killed long ago by robbers or eaten by wild animals.

"It was the Green Man who saved my life," was all that Claude would say.

His year away had changed the arrogant young man. Now he was hospitable to travelers. He cared for his animals. And each night Claude set out food and drink for the Green Man.

Name: _____ Date: _____

 **Activity**
23A

Literature Web

Directions: Complete the Literature Web for "The Green Man."

Key Words	**Feelings**
_____	_____
_____	_____
_____	_____
_____	_____

Title

_____

_____

_____

Ideas	**Images or Symbols**
_____	_____
_____	_____
_____	_____
_____	_____

**Activity
23B**

Illustrate Changes

Directions: In "The Green Man," Claude changes both inside and outside. Draw how you picture Claude at the beginning of the story. Then draw how you picture Claude when he tells the children that he is the Green Man.

Claude	The Green Man

Activity 23C

Vocabulary Web

Directions: Complete the Vocabulary Web for the word assigned to you.

Word Families	Synonyms	Antonyms

Dictionary Definition

Word

Analysis

Part of Speech

Origin

Sentence in Text

Stems

Student Example

Name: _____ Date: _____

Oral Presentation Evaluation Form

Speaker: _____ Assignment: _____

Directions: For items 1–10, circle the choice that describes the presentation. Then complete the two sentences.

Content

1. The purpose of the presentation was clear.

   Needs improvement   Satisfactory   Excellent

2. The speaker included details that supported the main idea.

   Needs improvement   Satisfactory   Excellent

3. The speaker showed knowledge of the subject.

   Needs improvement   Satisfactory   Excellent

4. The speaker used vocabulary that was rich and varied.

   Needs improvement   Satisfactory   Excellent

Organization

5. The speech followed the Hamburger Model, with a clear introduction, body, and conclusion.

   Needs improvement   Satisfactory   Excellent

6. The ideas flowed smoothly and in an orderly way.

   Needs improvement   Satisfactory   Excellent

7. The speaker closed the presentation with a strong, interesting idea that restated the purpose.

Needs improvement   Satisfactory   Excellent

Delivery

8. The speaker made good eye contact with the audience.

Needs improvement   Satisfactory   Excellent

9. The speaker spoke loudly enough for the entire audience to hear.

Needs improvement   Satisfactory   Excellent

10. The speaker's words were clear and could be understood.

Needs improvement   Satisfactory   Excellent

The best part of this presentation was:

_____

_____

_____

A suggestion for improvement is:

_____

_____

_____

"Nurse's Song" from *Songs of Innocence*

William Blake

When the voices of children are heard on the green
And laughing is heard on the hill,
My heart is at rest within my breast
And everything else is still.

"Then come home my children, the sun is gone down
And the dews of night arise;
Come come leave off play, and let us away
Till the morning appears in the skies."

"No no let us play, for it is yet day
And we cannot go to sleep;
Besides in the sky, the little birds fly
And the hills are all covered with sheep."

"Well well go & play till the light fades away
And then go home to bed."
The little ones leaped & shouted & laugh'd
And all the hills echoed.

"Nurse's Song" from *Songs of Experience*

William Blake

When the voices of children are heard on the green
And whisprings are in the dale:
The days of my youth rise fresh in my mind,
My face turns green and pale.

"Then come home my children, the sun is gone down
And the dews of night arise
Your spring & your day, are wasted in play
And your winter and night in disguise."

Name: _____ Date: _____

Compare and Contrast
Two Poems

Directions: Use the Venn diagram to compare and contrast the Nurse in the poem "Nurse's Song" from *Songs of Innocence* with the Nurse in the poem "Nurse's Song" from *Songs of Experience*. Write ways they are alike in the middle part of the diagram and ways they are different in the outer parts. Use only adjectives to describe the Nurse in each poem.

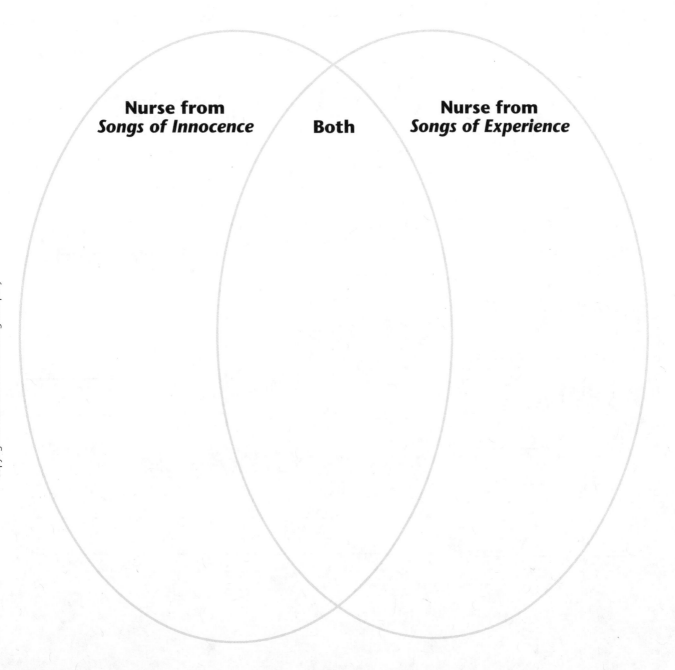

Nurse from
Songs of Innocence   Both   Nurse from
Songs of Experience

Activity
25B

Vocabulary Web

Directions: Complete the Vocabulary Web for the word assigned to you.

Word Families
_____
_____
_____
_____
_____

Synonyms
_____
_____

Antonyms
_____
_____

Dictionary Definition
_____
_____

Word
_____

Analysis

Part of Speech
_____

Stems
_____
_____
_____

Origin
_____
_____

Sentence in Text
_____
_____
_____
_____

Student Example
_____
_____

Name: _____ Date: _____

Discuss a Change
Generalization

Directions: Your group will be assigned a generalization about change. Discuss the generalization by thinking about the following question:

How have the experiences of this unit supported the generalization?

Answer the questions to help guide your discussion.

1. Generalization: _____

_____

_____

2. In which stories or poems was this generalization supported? How?

_____

_____

_____

_____

_____

_____

3. How have your experiences in this unit supported the generalization?

_____

_____

_____

_____

_____

4. Summarize how the experiences of this unit supported the generalization.

_____

_____

_____

_____

_____

_____

Name: _____ Date: _____

One Green Apple and the Change Generalizations

Directions: Describe how each generalization applies to the story *One Green Apple*.

1. Change is linked to time. (How is change linked to time?)

_____

_____

_____

2. Change may be positive or negative. (Does change always represent progress?)

_____

_____

_____

3. Change may be perceived as orderly or random. (Can we predict change?)

_____

_____

_____

4. Change is everywhere. (Does change apply to all areas of our world?)

_____

_____

_____

5. Change may happen naturally or may be caused by people. (What causes change?)

_____

_____

_____

Name: _____ Date: _____

Literature Web

Directions: Complete the Literature Web for *One Green Apple*.

Key Words
_____
_____
_____
_____
_____

Feelings
_____
_____
_____
_____
_____

Title
_____
_____
_____

Ideas
_____
_____
_____
_____

Images or Symbols
_____
_____
_____
_____

Name: _____ Date: _____

Activity
26D
Final Writing Assignment

Directions: Think about how the readings in this unit have reflected the generalizations about change. Select one generalization that seemed especially true to you in the readings and write it in the blanks. List examples of how the generalization is shown to be true in the readings. Use at least three different stories or poems from the unit.

Generalization:

_____

_____

_____

Examples:

_____

_____

_____

_____

_____

_____

Copyright © Kendall Hunt Publishing Company

Write a persuasive paragraph arguing that the generalization that you selected is true, based on the examples from the readings. State your opinion about the issue, then give at least three reasons showing evidence that the generalization is true. Explain your reasons. Write a conclusion to end your paragraph.

_____

_____

_____

_____

_____

_____

_____

_____

_____

_____

_____

_____

Name: _____ Date: _____

Activity
26E

Apple Math

Directions: Use the information to help you answer each question.

One pound of apples is either:

4 small apples

3 medium apples

or 2 large apples

1. About 2 pounds of apples are needed to make one 9-inch pie. How many medium apples are needed to make a 9-inch pie?

    _____

2. A bushel of apples weighs about 42 pounds. About how many apples are in a bushel of large apples?

    _____

3. One pound of apples is equal to 3 cups of diced apples. If a recipe calls for 6 cups of diced apples, how many small apples do you need?

    _____

4. A recipe calls for 9 cups of sliced apples. If one pound of apples is about 3 cups of sliced apples, how many pounds of small apples do you need for the recipe?

    _____

Copyright © Kendall Hunt Publishing Company

Journeys and Destinations · Lesson 26 · Closing Discussion of the Concept of Change

The Miser

A fable by Aesop

A Miser had buried his gold in a secret place in his garden. Every day he went to the spot, dug up the treasure and counted it piece by piece to make sure it was all there. He made so many trips that a Thief, who had been observing him, guessed what it was the Miser had hidden, and one night quietly dug up the treasure and made off with it.

When the Miser discovered his loss, he was overcome with grief and despair. He groaned and cried and tore his hair.

A passerby heard his cries and asked what had happened.

"My gold! O my gold!" cried the Miser, wildly, "someone has robbed me!"

"Your gold! There in that hole? Why did you put it there? Why did you not keep it in the house where you could easily get it when you had to buy things?"

"Buy!" screamed the Miser angrily. "Why, I never touched the gold. I couldn't think of spending any of it."

The stranger picked up a large stone and threw it into the hole.

"If that is the case," he said, "cover up that stone. It is worth just as much to you as the treasure you lost!"

A possession is worth no more than the use we make of it.

Activity
27A

Literature Web

Directions: Complete the Literature Web for "The Miser."

Key Words
_____
_____
_____
_____

Feelings
_____
_____
_____
_____

Title
_____
_____
_____

Ideas
_____
_____
_____
_____

Images or Symbols
_____
_____
_____
_____